SCHOLASTIC COLLECTIONS

Compiled by Wes Magee

Poetry

© 1992 Scholastic Ltd
6789   890123

Published by Scholastic Ltd,
Villiers House,
Clarendon Avenue,
Leamington Spa,
Warwickshire CV32 5PR

Compiler Wes Magee
Editor Christine Lee
Sub editor Jane Wright
Series designer Joy White
Designer Elizabeth Harrison
Cover and illustrations Merida Woodford

Designed using Aldus Pagemaker
Processed by Salvo Design and Print, Leamington Spa
Artwork by David Harban Design, Warwick

British Library Cataloguing-in-Publication Data
A catalogue record for this book is
available from the British Library.

ISBN 0-590-53021-6

Contents

UP AND AWAY

PEOPLE, PEOPLE, PEOPLE

THE MODERN WORLD

THROUGH THE YEAR

SCHOOL DAYS

LIVING ON THE LAND

Houses

Where would you live if you were me?
A lonely lighthouse in the sea
With a garden of waves and rocks?
A narrowboat nosing through locks?
A windmill with a winding stair
And round rooms stacked like building blocks –
Would you live there?

Where would I live if I were you?
A wooden ark, a floating zoo.
A swaying eyrie in a tree
Would do for me.
An igloo with an icy dome,
A painted gypsy caravan,
A paper palace in Japan
Could be my home.

Sue Cowling

This is the chimney

This is the chimney all askew. This is the roof that has a tilt. These are the walls the wind blows through. This is the house that Jerry built.

Jenny Morris

The filthy, dirty house

Filthy, dirty house.
Everyone would grouse
If they had to live inside
The filthy, dirty house.

Twelve piles of ironing
Waiting to be pressed;
Sheets, shirts, jeans, skirts,
Granny's old string vest.

Eleven lots of washing-up
Standing in the sink.
Ten dirty ash-trays
Adding to the stink.

Nine broken biscuits
Trampled on the mat.
Eight chewed-up fishbones
Left there by the cat.

Seven screwed-up newspapers
Strewn across the stairs.
Six scruffy Cindy dolls
Covered in dog's hairs.

Five deep-fried fish-cakes,
Fallen on the floor.
Four filthy fingermarks
Smeared across the door.

Three thousand sewing threads
Thrown against the wall.
Two sweaty, squash socks
Sitting in the hall.

One piece of buttered bread,
Nibbled by a mouse.
In the very, very, very, *very*
Filthy, dirty house.

Ian Larmont

I remember, I remember

I remember, I remember
The house where I was born,
The little window where the sun
Came peeping in at morn;
He never came a wink too soon
Nor brought too long a day;
But now, I often wish the night
Had borne my breath away.

I remember, I remember
The roses, red and white,
The violets, and the lily-cups –
Those flowers made of light!
The lilacs where the robin built,
And where my brother set
The laburnum on his birthday –
The tree is living yet!

I remember, I remember
Where I was used to swing,
And thought the air must rush as fresh
To swallows on the wing;
My spirit flew in feathers then
That is so heavy now,
The summer pools could hardly cool
The fever on my brow.

I remember, I remember
The fir-trees dark and high;
I used to think their slender tops
Were close against the sky:
It was a childish ignorance,
But now 'tis little joy
To know I'm farther off from Heaven
Than when I was a boy.

Thomas Hood

Up inside the attic

Climb the shaking ladder,
Slide the rusty catch,
Brush away the cobwebs,
Wriggle through the hatch,
Balance on the rafters –
Inches from the sky –
Up inside the attic
Where the old things lie.

Here's a creaking suitcase
Crammed with secret things:
Lacy gloves and corsets,
Jars of curtain rings,
Collars, puppets, marbles,
Picture books as well,
Glittering Christmas tinsel
And a small brass bell.

Over in the shadows
Worn-out teddy bears
Lost in dreams of picnics
Snooze on broken chairs;
Shining high above them
Something seems to glow –
Just the dusty moonface
Of an old banjo.

What's this thing with handles?
What's that thing with feet?
Who left the fourteen bed-springs
Underneath this sheet?
Look! A box of comics.
Look! A crate of toys.
What was that? Sh! Listen!
Something made a noise!

Quick! Across the rafters,
Wriggle through the hatch,
Down the shaking ladder,
Don't forget the catch,
Was there someone up there?
Probably just a mouse,
Couldn't be a nasty
In this nice old house.

There's the hall clock chiming:
Time for bed. Goodnight.
See you in the morning,
Happy dreams, sleep tight.
We'll go back tomorrow
Bravely, you and I,
Up inside the attic
Where the old things lie.

Richard Edwards

Secret

Down Tanhouse Lane by the old silver birch
A spotty, red lady was spying on you,
Deep in a crack of the old silver bark,
Secretly spying where nobody knew,
– Except a black rook in the old silver tree
And Susie and Rose who showed her to me.

Cynthia Mitchell

In the kitchen

In the kitchen,
After the aimless
Chatter of the plates,
The murmurings of the gas,
The chuckle of the water pipes
And the sharp exchanges
Of knives, forks and spoons,
Comes the serious quiet,
When the sink slowly clears its throat
And you can hear the occasional rumble
Of the refrigerator's tummy
As it digests the cold.

John Cotton

From the winter wind

From the winter wind
a cold fly
came to our window
where we had frozen our noses
and warmed his feet on the glass.

Michael Rosen

Sixteen steps to the ice-house

SIXTEEN steps to the ice-house
BLACK with slime-slither mould,
SIXTEEN steps to the dungeon depths
AND that petrifying cold
THAT holds the souls of servants
LIKE breath afraid to breathe
LEST it disturbs some sinewy shape –
NOT of this century.
CLATTER! as rat-scattered bones
SHATTER the stagnant still,
ECHO empty tunes to the dead
WHO guard, in ghostly chill,
SIXTEEN steps *from* the ice-house
BLACK with slime-slither mould,
SIXTEEN steps *from* the dungeon depths
AND that petrifying cold.

Gina Douthwaite

The amphibious hippopotamus

THE AMPHIBIOUS HIPPOPOTAMUS
JUST PRETENDS TO SWIM
AT THE WATER'S RIM
IN FACT TROTS INSTEAD
ON THE RIVER BED

Jenny Morris

from...To a butterfly

I've watched you now a full half-hour,
Self-poised upon that yellow flower;
And, little butterfly, indeed
I know not if you sleep or feed.
How motionless! – not frozen seas
More motionless! and then
What joy awaits you, when the breeze
Has found you out among the trees,
And calls you forth again!

William Wordsworth

Hurt no living thing

Hurt no living thing:
Ladybird, nor butterfly,
Nor moth with dusty wing,
Nor cricket chirping cheerily,
Nor grasshopper so light of leap,
Nor dancing gnat, nor beetle fat,
Nor harmless worms that creep.

Christina Rossetti

Insect noises

The quiet kingdom of insects:
The hushed hiss of a spider's web-spinning,
The subdued snores of a sleeping beetle,
The deliberate tip-toeing of a considerate ant,
The delicate flutterings of evening mayflies,
The silent glidings of powdery-winged moths,
The ladybird quietly counting her spots.

John Cotton

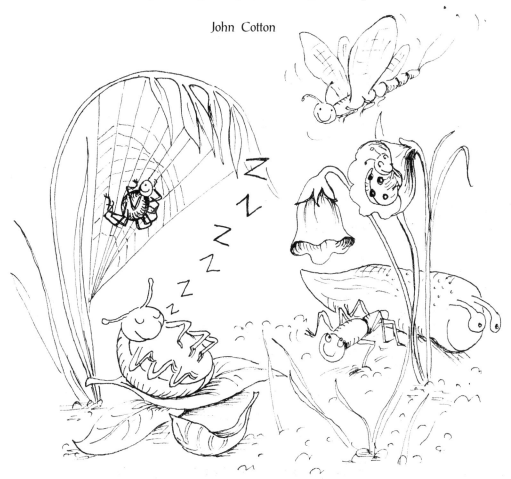

Bag of mixed candy

Liquorice slugs and ladybird smarties,
Lemonade wasps and peppermint snails,
Humbugging worms of wriggly spearmint,
And right at the bottom five fizzy frogs tails.

Theresa Heine

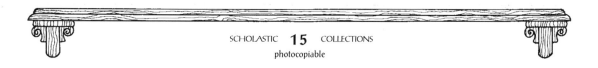

Creatures on the move

Centipedes come marching
on their hundred tiny feet
Field-mice scurry
Through the golden fields of wheat

Frogs leap, hip-hop
Blue whales belly-flop

Coloured insects creep and crawl
Cockerels swagger, proud and tall
Snakes slither
Jelly-fish quiver
Hedgehogs, rolling like a ball

Parrots perch
Elephants lurch
Seagulls swoop and dive
Cheetahs chase
Rabbits race
And jitter-bugs jive!

    Cats pounce
        Kangaroos bounce
                Peacocks dance
                        Ponies prance

Gliding and
              sliding!
    Slouching and
                   crouching!
            Swooping and
                     looping!

Our world is full of creatures
Intent on where they're going
But how they choose to get there
...there's no sure way of knowing!

Jo Vernillo

from...The Pied Piper of Hamelin

Rats!
They fought the dogs, and killed the cats,
And bit the babies in the cradles,
And ate the cheeses out of the vats,
And licked the soup from the cooks' own ladles,
Split open the kegs of salted sprats,
Made nests inside men's Sunday hats,
And even spoiled the women's chats,
By drowning their speaking
With shrieking and squeaking
In fifty different sharps and flats.

Robert Browning

The snail

To grass, or leaf, or fruit, or wall,
The Snail sticks fast, nor fears to fall,
As if he grew there, house and all
                                    Together.

Within that house secure he hides,
When danger imminent betides
Or storms, or other harms besides,
                                    Of weather.

Give but his horns the slightest touch,
His self-collecting power is such,
He shrinks into his house with much
                                    Displeasure.

Where'er he dwells, he dwells alone,
Except himself has chattels none,
Well satisfied to be his own
                                    Whole treasure.

Thus hermit-like, his life he leads,
Nor partner of his Banquet needs,
And if he meets one, only feeds
                                    The faster.

Who seeks him must be worse than blind
(He and his house are so combined)
If, finding it, he fails to find
                                    Its master.

William Cowper

Sleeping cats

Cats dedicate
their lives
to dozing,

stretched out like
pulled gum before
the gas fire,

parcelled up,
legs folded away
like stored tent poles,

tail tucked under,
slitted eyes watching
what will happen next,

curled into doughnuts
on doorsteps,
on walls and window ledges,

drowsing,
too hot to purr,
in smelted sunlight,

snoozing, half-awake,
murpling in ecstasy
on lazy laps,

or lying heavy
as bags of cement
on warm beds

in the murk of night,
deeply asleep,
for once.

Like Eskimos
with all their words
for whiteness,

cats have dozens
of different ways
of sleeping.

Moira Andrew

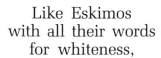

Choosing their names

Our old cat has kittens three –
What do you think their names should be?

One is tabby with emerald eyes,
    And a tail that's long and slender.
And into a temper she quickly flies
    If you ever by chance offend her.
        I think we shall call her this –
        I think we shall call her that –
Now, don't you think that Pepperpot
    Is a nice name for a cat?

One is black with a frill of white,
    And her feet are all white fur,
If you stroke her she carries her tail upright
    And quickly begins to purr.
        I think we shall call her this –
        I think we shall call her that –
Now, don't you think that Sootikin
    Is a nice name for a cat?

One is a tortoiseshell yellow and black,
    With plenty of white about him;
If you tease him, at once he sets up his back,
    He's a quarrelsome one, ne'er doubt him.
        I think we shall call him this –
        I think we shall call him that –
Now, don't you think that Scratchaway
    Is a nice name for a cat?

Our old cat has kittens three
And I fancy these their names will be:
Pepperpot, Sootikin, Scratchaway – there!
Were ever kittens with these to compare?
And we call the old mother –
    Now, what do you think?
Tabitha Longclaws Tiddley Wink.

Thomas Hood

The Tyger

Tyger! Tyger! burning bright
In the forests of the night,
What immortal hand or eye
Could frame thy fearful symmetry?

In what distant deeps or skies
Burnt the fire of thine eyes?
On what wings dare he aspire?
What the hand dare seize the fire?

And what shoulder, and what art,
Could twist the sinews of thy heart?
And, when thy heart began to beat,
What dread hand? and what dread feet?

What the hammer? what the chain?
In what furnace was thy brain?
What the anvil? what dread grasp
Dare its deadly terrors clasp?

When the stars threw down their spears,
And watered Heaven with their tears,
Did He smile His work to see?
Did He who made the Lamb make thee?

Tyger! Tyger! burning bright
In the forests of the night,
What immortal hand or eye
Dare frame thy fearful symmetry?

William Blake

Lions

Near an ancient standing Baobab tree
the lion sits with burning mane.
He looks all around
but makes no sounds,
in the heat of the African plain.

Behind, in the grey and cooling shade,
the rest of the pride is lying.
After the kill
they have eaten their fill
and now sleep the safe sleep of the lion.

Tomorrow they will awaken refreshed,
as a new day breaks over the plain,
and they'll sleekly rise
with death in their eyes,
to start the hunt over again.

Robin Mellor

Badgers

Badgers come creeping from dark under ground,
Badgers scratch hard with a bristly sound,
Badgers go nosing around.

Badgers have whiskers and black and white faces,
Badger cubs scramble and scrap and run races,
Badgers like overgrown places.

Badgers don't jump when a vixen screams,
Badgers drink quietly from moonshiny streams,
Badgers dig holes in our dreams.

Badgers are working while you and I sleep,
Pushing their tunnels down twisting and steep,
Badgers have secrets to keep.

Richard Edwards

Labrador

A lumbering detective
is the labrador.
Greedily sniffing out
the wren's poor hiding place
she will risk a brambled nose.

She enjoys producing panic
as she plunders all the bushes,
stealing secrets
in the wagging of her tail.

A blundering detective
is the labrador.
The squirrels see her coming
and scamper to safety
with the crows.

Returning home,
she is a sleeping heap
where her dreams are thunder
and bones.

Celia Warren

The world with its countries

The world with its countries,
Mountains and seas,
People and creatures,
Flowers and trees,
The fish in the waters,
The birds in the air
Are calling to ask us
All to take care.

These are our treasures,
A gift from above,
We should say thank you
With a care that shows love
For the blue of the ocean,
The clearness of air,
The wonder of forests
And the valleys so fair.

The song of the skylark,
The warmth of the sun,
The rushing of clear streams
And new life begun
Are gifts we should cherish,
So join in the call
To strive to preserve them
For the future of all.

John Cotton

from...Kubla Khan

In Xanadu did Kubla Khan
A stately pleasure-dome decree;
Where Alph, the sacred river, ran
Through caverns measureless to man
Down to a sunless sea.
So twice five miles of fertile ground
With walls and towers were girdled round;
And there were gardens bright with sinuous rills
Where blossomed many an incense-bearing tree;
And here were forests ancient as the hills,
Enfolding sunny spots of greenery.

Samuel Taylor Coleridge

The flower-fed buffaloes

The flower-fed buffaloes of the spring
In the days of long ago,
Ranged where the locomotives sing
And the prairie flowers lie low:–
The tossing, blooming, perfumed grass
Is swept away by the wheat,
Wheels and wheels and wheels spin by
In the spring that still is sweet.
But the flower-fed buffaloes of the spring
Left us, long ago.
They gore no more, they bellow no more,
They trundle around the hills no more:–
With the Blackfeet, lying low,
With the Pawnees, lying low,
Lying low.

Vachel Lindsay

Dancing teepees

Dancing teepees
High up in the Rocky Mountains
Dancing teepees
Dance on the grassy banks of Cripple Creek
With laughing fringes in the autumn sun.
Indian children
Play with bows and arrows
On the grassy banks of Cripple Creek.
Indian women
Gather kindling
To start an evening fire.

Dancing teepees
Dance against fire-lighted autumn trees.
Braves returning
Home from raiding,
Gallantly ride into camp
With horses, scalps, and ornaments.
Dancing teepees
Sleep now on the grassy banks of Cripple Creek
High up in the Rocky Mountains.

Calvin O'John (Ute-Navajo)

Learning the flowers

Along the lanes, down sunny hours,
That summer Granny taught me flowers:
Dog rose, foxglove, lady's smock,
Ox-eye daisy, townhall clock,
Billy's button, adder's meat,
Old man's beard and meadowsweet.
Sometimes I went to pick, but she
Smiled and said gently, 'Let them be.'
Sticky Willy, bugle, pansy,
Yellow rattle, harebell, tansy,
Silverweed and tormentil:
She taught me and I know them still.

Eric Finney

What is a weed?

A bramble,
sweet with blackberries?
A wild rose,
sharp with thorns?
A nettle,
hung with butterflies?
A daisy,
starring lawns?

A dandelion,
lighting May?
A clover,
tipped with bees?
An ivy,
creeping round a shed?
Are *these*
really *weeds*?

Judith Nicholls

Lupins

I've lately developed
a longing for lupins;
have even dug the bed,
and planted seeds,
and faithfully watered them:
lupins filling my head.

Colourful spikes
with a twist in the tail,
and leaves like shaking hands,
with sweetly scented
nostalgic nectar,
familiar floral friends.

I've just rediscovered
a loving for lupins;
remembering them by the
   shed,
where my toes would touch
from the garden swing,
and lupins bowed me to bed.

Celia Warren

A spring flower riddle

As our simple wintry name implies –
A fall of crystal whiteness from the skies.

(Snowdrops)

Our golden trumpets shout loud and strong –
Winter's gone! Spring won't be long!

(Daffodils)

Tiny goblets of yellow, mauve and blue –
These little cups collect the morning dew.

(Crocuses)

On grassy banks our prim, creamy flowers
Bring a burst of colour after April's showers.

(Primroses)

Million upon million tiny fairy bells
Make a bright blue carpet in the woodland dells.

(Bluebells)

I grow by the roadside, sun-yellow flowers.
When my petals are gone I blow away the hours.

(Dandelions)

Tiny white stars chain-stitched across the lawn.
Called the day's eye; wide-eyed from early dawn.

(Daisies)

I hide in the woodland, shy and tiny by the hedge.
Sweet-scented – I'm a colour at the rainbow's edge.

(Violets)

Put altogether we make a Spring Bouquet –
But where we live is where we love to stay.

David Whitehead

The demon-tree

When I was young
there was a tree...
Oh, how it used to frighten me.

It rose up, huge and fierce,
out of the flat Suffolk fields
and if I saw it in the distance,
my heart would leap into my throat.
I'd hurry by, eyes down, hoping
that the ugly, gnarled demon-tree,
with outstretched claws,
would not catch me!

But one wild, windy night
I'd stayed too long at school, was late,
hurrying home across the fields,
driven back by lashing rain and razor-winds,
I found myself huddled under that tree
feeling its strong, brown arms protecting me:
daring the rain to make me wet —
the wind to whistle through.
They kept their distance.

Its twisted trunk and knotted limbs
kept me safe and warm
until Dad found me
and took me home.

Jo Vernillo

Apple song

Down along the orchard,
Such a happy din
As through the dappled sunlight
We bring the apples in.
Apples red, apples green,
Apples russet-brown.
Spread the nets, and climb the trees,
And shake the apples down!

Boys are up the ladders
Girls are in the grass;
And everyone is laughing
As the golden hours pass.
Apples red, apples green,
Apples russet-brown.
Spread the nets, and climb the trees,
And shake the apples down!

Clive Sansom

Fruit salad

Apples
make cider,
bananas – milk shake,
oranges – squash,
plums – tummy ache.
Gooseberry bake
green frogspawn pie
but brambles
paint fingers
liko bruisos
with dye.

Pears
cry in drops
round raspberry cake,
sliced lemon swims
in a lemonade lake.
Strawberries quake
in jelly, and jam
but TOMATO'S
the fruit that
tastos bost
with ham.

Gina Douthwaite

Eat up! Eat up!

My sister, for breakfast,
eats fried eggs, bacon, fried bread,
tomatoes, mushrooms, and then
drinks coffee...cup after cup.
'Come on,' she says to me,
'Eat up! Eat up!'

My brother, for lunch,
gobbles salad, stacks of sandwiches,
a squadron of sausages on sticks, and then
swigs mug after mug of strong tea.
'Hey you!' he says, 'eat up!
You're skinny as a flea!'

My dad, every evening,
devours lamp chops, carrots, cabbage,
dozens of new potatoes, and then
polishes off a rice pudding for dinner.
'Eat up!' he orders.
'You're getting thinner and *thinner*!'

But I'm not greedy.
Enough is enough for me.
It's crazy
to stuff yourself solid
with food.

Don't you agree?

Wes Magee

Picnic lunch

I like blackcurrant jam,
I like it on my bread.
But so do wasps and bees.
'May I have tuna fish instead?

Please.'

Janis Priestley

Shush

Oh DO be quiet Abeline
Children shouldn't be heard, only seen,
And all you can do is stand and scream,
Just because your salad's not quite clean!

Look at the SLUG that made you yell.
He's riding a radish remarkably well,
Weaving a sluggy spiral spell
so quietly – while you just YELL!

Marnie Francis

Who made the pie?

Who made the pie?
I did.

Who stole the pie?
He did.

Who found the pie?
She did.

Who ate the pie?
You did.

Who cried for pie?
We all did.

Anonymous

Choosing a bag of crisps

'I eat prawn cocktail flavour most.'
'I don't. They're foul. They're gross.'

'What about barbecued steak?'
'They taste absolutely fake.'

'How about onion with cheese?'
'They'll do...at a squeeze.'

'Well, what *do* you want this time?'
'Hedgehog flavour with extra spine!'

Janis Priestley

The food that gets stuck in the plug of the sink

A soggy tomato
    and yesterday's peas,
a dried up sultana,
    a lump of green cheese!

It's juicy, it's fruity,
    it's green and it's pink,
the food that gets stuck
    in the plug of the sink.

Tea bags and spinach,
    bananas and beans,
some pasta and peelings,
    a pig's intestines.

It's juicy, it's fruity,
    it's green and it's pink,
the food that gets stuck
    in the plug of the sink.

Mushrooms and meatballs,
    a pineapple chunk,
a fried egg and gravy,
    a sausage that sunk!

It's juicy, it's fruity,
    it's green and it's pink,
the food that gets stuck
    in the plug of the sink.

John Rice

Stegosaurus

I have a stegosaurus.
He's really rather sweet.
But he's very, very fussy
About the food he'll eat.

I offered him a burger,
A plate of egg and chips,
A dish of chicken curry,
But none would pass his lips.

I asked, 'What would be tasty?
I'll get it if I can.'
He said, 'I'd better tell you,
I'm a Vegetarian!'

Wendy Larmont

WHERE THERE'S WATER

Underwater, holding nose

Underwater, holding nose,
dive,
dive,
down he goes.
Eerie noises, heartbeat beating,
water pipes
and central heating.
Gliding forward, no one knows,
Along the slimy bath he goes.

Distant voices,
bubbles rise,
stinging water, screwed up eyes.
Cheeks are bulging, pressure grows.
Wrinkled fingers,
crinkled toes.
Surface quickly,
come up clean...
He's the human submarine.

Jez Alborough

After a bath

After my bath
I try, try, try
to wipe myself
till I'm dry, dry, dry.

Hands to wipe
and fingers and toes
and two wet legs
and a shiny nose.

Just think how much
less time I'd take
if I were a dog
and could shake, shake, shake.

Aileen Fisher

Bubblebath

I make my body disappear,
Grow a long white beard from ear to ear.
I clear a path through endless snow
wrapped up in fur like an eskimo.
I carve a statue, shape a stone
And build a pyramid on my own.
I whip up frothy syllabub,
Meringue and soufflé – in my tub!
I bring storms like the weatherman,
Pile clouds on Crete, Corfu and Cannes.
A twenty-one bubble salute
Is taken in my birthday-suit!

Sue Cowling

Water

When Joe so loves water for sloshing,
and splashing,
and splishing,
and sploshing,
And sailing,
and sinking,
And bailing,
and drinking,
Why does he so hate it for washing?

Cynthia Mitchell

Water cycle

☆ Riding on high,   Clouds in the sky
All over again.   Looking like paper
Ready to rain   But made up of vapour,
Into the skies   Drift over hills
Then the mists rise   Where the air chills.
By the sun's rays.   Vapour condenses,
Of watery haze   Rainfall commences
Allows the creation   (Or dew on the grass
And evaporation   Like breath on a glass)
Gradually heats it   This trickles to give us
There the sun greets it   Streamlets and rivers
It reaches the seas.   Till by degrees

☆ start

Noel Petty

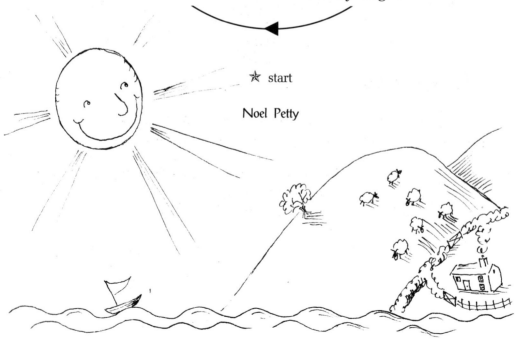

raindrops and rainbows

splash, hear the raindrops
    in the puddle

shimmer, see the rainbow
    in the bubble

splatter, hear the water
    in the bath

speckle, see the snowflakes
    on the path

flicker, feel my fingers
    in the rainy-wet grass

Joan Poulson

Rainbow

R ain and sun together make the rainbow grow
A rching in the cloudy sky, see the colours glow
I ndigo and violet, bands of red and blue
N ow it's bold and brilliant, then it fades from view
B ridge of coloured ribbons – magic to behold
O ver field and factory...over wood and wold
W here the rainbow comes to earth
                 – there's the crock of gold

David Whitehead

Weathers

This is the weather the cuckoo likes,
    And so do I;
When showers betumble the chestnut spikes,
    And nestlings fly;
And the little brown nightingale bills his best,
And they sit outside at 'The Travellers' Rest',
And maids come forth sprig-muslin drest,
And citizens dream of the south and west,
    And so do I.

This is the weather the shepherd shuns,
    And so do I;
When beeches drip in brown and duns,
    And thresh, and ply;
And hill-hid tides throb, throe on throe,
And meadow rivulets overflow,
And drops on gate-bars hang in a row,
And rooks in families homeward go,
    And so do I.

Thomas Hardy

Reflections in a pond

A
tree
by a pond
reflected on
its annual crop of
gold
y f
s i
l s
ɟ h
gold
its annual crop of
reflected on
by a pond
tree
A

Carol Coiffait

The lake

On a calm day
The lake
Imagines it is a mirror
And smiles back
At people who pass by
Smiling.

On a breezy day
The lake
Hunches its shoulders
And sends ripples
Scudding across the surface.

On a winter's day
The lake
Hides itself
Under a frozen blanket
And refuses to budge
Until it is warm enough
To come out again.

John Foster

The Loch Ness Monster

The Loch Ness Monster is a myth:
Is the loch without? Or is it with?

If Nessie's there, why can't we see
A hump or two — or maybe three!

Peter Thabit Jones

The river's story

I remember when life was good.
I shilly-shallied across meadows,
Tumbled down mountains,
I laughed and gurgled through woods,
Stretched and yawned in a myriad of floods.
Insects, weightless as sunbeams,
Settled upon my skin to drink.
I wore lily-pads like medals.
Fish, lazy and battle-scarred,
Gossiped beneath them.
The damselflies were my ballerinas,
The pike my ambassadors.
Kingfishers, disguised as rainbows,
Were my secret agents.
It was a sweet time, a gone-time,
A time before factories grew,
Brick by greedy brick,
And left me cowering
In monstrous shadows.
Like drunken giants
They vomited their poisons into me.
Tonight a scattering of vagrant bluebells,
Dwarfed by the same poisons,
Toll my ending.
Children, come and find me if you wish,
I am your inheritance.
Behind the derelict housing-estates
You will discover my remnants.
Clogged with garbage and junk
To an open sewer I've shrunk.
I, who have flowed through history,
Who have seen hamlets become villages,
Villages become towns, towns become cities,
Am reduced to a trickle of filth
Beneath the still, burning stars.

Brian Patten

What are heavy?

What are heavy? sea-sand and sorrow:
What are brief? today and tomorrow:
What are frail? Spring blossoms and youth:
What are deep? the ocean and truth.

Christina Rossetti

Slowly

Slowly the tide creeps up the sand,
Slowly the shadows cross the land.
Slowly the cart-horse pulls his mile,
Slowly the old man mounts the stile.

Slowly the hands move round the clock,
Slowly the dew dries on the dock.
Slow is the snail – but slowest of all
The green moss spreads on the old brick wall.

James Reeves

Beachcomber

Monday I found a boot –
Rust and salt leather.
I gave it back to the sea, to dance in.

Tuesday a spar of timber worth thirty bob.
Next winter
It will be a chair, a coffin, a bed.

Wednesday a half can of Swedish spirits.
I tilted my head.
The shore was cold with mermaids and angels.

Thursday I got nothing, seaweed,
A whale bone,
Wet feet and a loud cough.

Friday I held a seaman's skull,
Sand spilling from it
The way time is told on kirkyard stones.

Saturday a barrel of sodden oranges.
A Spanish ship
Was wrecked last month at The Kame.

Sunday, for fear of the elders,
I sit on my bum.
What's heaven? A sea chest with a thousand
gold coins.

George Mackay Brown

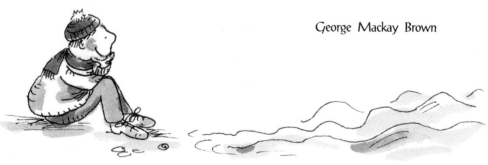

The tide rises, the tide falls

The tide rises, the tide falls,
The twilight darkens, the curlew calls;
Along the sea-sands damp and brown
The traveller hastens towards the town,
    And the tide rises, the tide falls.

Darkness settles on roofs and walls,
But the sea, the sea in the darkness calls;
The little waves, with their soft white hands,
Efface the footprints in the sands,
And the tide rises, the tide falls.

The morning breaks; the steeds in their stalls
Stamp and neigh, as the hostler calls;
The day returns, but nevermore
Returns the traveller to the shore,
    And the tide rises, the tide falls.

Henry Wadsworth Longfellow

At the seaside

When I was down beside the sea
A wooden spade they gave to me
    To dig the sandy shore.
My holes were empty like a cup,
In every hole the sea came up
    Till it could come no more.

Robert Louis Stevenson

Our super sand-castle

We built a super sand-castle
Peter, Jane and I.
With turrets tall
And towers pointing to the sky.
We heaped it high
We built it strong,
With walls so square and thick.
Jane scooped out tiny windows
With a little lolly stick.
Peter made a drawbridge
From a piece of sea-washed wood.
I dug a moat
With both my hands
As deeply as I could.
At last the work was finished;
Just one more job to do,
To buy a flag for the castle top,
A flag red, white and blue.
So off we ran along the beach
Peter, Jane and I,
To the little shop
By the ice-cream van
Our castle flag to buy.
We thought how fine our flag would look
Atop the highest wall.
Our sand-castle would really be
The grandest one of all.
So quickly back we ran, we three,
To where we'd played all day
To find – Oh Dear!
The sea had come and washed our dream away.

So tomorrow we'll build a bigger one,
Peter, Jane and I.
With turrets and with towers
And – a flag – to raise on high.

David Whitehead

This is my rock

This is my rock,
And here I run
To steal the secret of the sun;

This is my rock
And here come I
Before the night has swept the sky;

This is my rock,
This is the place
I meet the evening face to face.

David McCord

Sea timeless song

Hurricane come
and hurricane go
but sea – sea timeless
sea timeless
sea timeless
sea timeless
sea timeless

Hibiscus bloom
then dry-wither so
but sea – sea timeless
sea timeless
sea timeless
sea timeless
sea timeless

Tourist come
and tourist go
but sea – sea timeless
sea timeless
sea timeless
sea timeless
sea timeless

Grace Nichols

Let's hear it for the limpet

If there's one animal that isn't a wimp, it
Is the limpet.

Let me provide an explanation
For my admiration.

To start with, it's got two thousand tiny teeth
Beneath

Its comical conical-hat-shaped, greeny-grey shell:
A tongue as well

That rasps the delicate seaweed through its front door:
What's more –

And this is what gives me the greatest surprise –
Two bright eyes

Indoors at the end of long tentacles poking out, which
Twitch.

But its funniest feature by far is its foot
That's put

Straight down to clamp it fast to the rock.
(Gulls knock,

You see, at the shell to try to winkle it off
For scoff.)

But the limpet does more with its foot than Ian Rush.
Forsaking the crush

Of its home life it stomps off, foraging, humping its
shell with it,
Then thinks, 'The hell with it,'

And slithers back to exactly where it began.
What a man

is the limpet, in his wilderness of weed!

Needless to say, they make very good pets indeed.

Kit Wright

Exploring the rock pool

We explore the rock pool
A small world of its own:
The scuttling crab, quick shrimps,
Sea-polished stone
With hints of colours
Enhanced by the light-
Refracting water
Making all so bright.
The strands of seaweed
Verdant, sleek as silk,
The tiny limpets,
Shells as white as milk.
A sea in miniature
Which lasts just for a day,
When the tide renews it
Washing the old away.

John Cotton

Sea seasons

The sea bounces
over barnacles,
bobbing and buckling
in the springtime breeze.

The sea slithers
across shingle,
splintering and sparkling
under a bright summer sun.

The sea prowls
over pebbles,
pimpling and prickling
on damp autumn days.

The sea rushes
across rocks,
ranting and raving
when winter winds blow.

Moira Andrew

Wreckers' Beach

I walk along the Wreckers' Beach
where cobbler, farm-hand, fisherwife,
placed lamps to welcome lost ships
on to the angry, razor rocks.

Oystercatchers harshly remember
the haunting screams of dying sailors,
the afternoon breeze puffs in my hair,
small brother to the mad storm wind.

I find no boxes of silks, no
bags of gold, strings of pearls,
no corpses with wet pockets and purses
to rifle greedily for coin.

My treasures are more simple,
a few shells, a streaky pebble,
a twisted driftwood root, yet
the gulls shrilly protest my plunder

with accusing calls, one to the other,
as if I had tempted the flotsam
up to the tideline of seaweed and sand,
on the lonely Wreckers' Beach.

Robin Mellor

A smuggler's song

If you wake at midnight, and hear a horse's feet,
Don't go drawing back the blind, or looking in the street,
Them that asks no questions isn't told a lie.
Watch the wall, my darling, while the Gentlemen go by!
       Five and twenty ponies
       Trotting through the dark —
       Brandy for the Parson
       'Baccy for the Clerk;
       Laces for a lady, letters for a spy,
And watch the wall, my darling, while the Gentlemen go by!

Running round the woodlump if you should chance to find
Little barrels, roped and tarred, all full of brandy-wine,
Don't you shout to come and look, nor use 'em for your play.
Put the brushwood back again — and they'll be gone next day!

If you see the stable-door setting open wide;
If you see a tired horse lying down inside;
If your mother mends a coat cut about and tore;
If the lining's wet and warm — don't you ask no more!

If you meet King George's men, dressed in blue and red,
You be careful what you say, and mindful what is said.
If they call you 'pretty maid', and chuck you 'neath the chin,
Don't you tell where no one is, nor yet where no one's been!

Knocks and footsteps round the house — whistles after dark —
You've no call for running out till the house-dogs bark.
Trusty's here, and *Pincher's* here, and see how dumb they lie —
They don't fret to follow when the Gentlemen go by!

If you do as you've been told, likely there's a chance,
You'll be give a dainty doll, all the way from France,
With a cap of Valenciennes, and a velvet hood —
A present from the Gentlemen, along o' being good!
       Five and twenty ponies
       Trotting through the dark —
       Brandy for the Parson,
       'Baccy for the Clerk.
Them that asks no questions isn't told a lie —
Watch the wall, my darling, while the Gentlemen go by!

Rudyard Kipling

Above the dock

Above the quiet dock in midnight,
Tangled in the tall mast's corded height,
Hangs the moon. What seemed so far away
Is but a child's balloon, forgotten after play.

T.E. Hulme

Over the sea to Skye

Sing me a song of a lad that is gone,
Say, could that lad be I?
Merry of soul he sailed on a day
Over the sea to Skye.

Mull was astern, Rhum on the port,
Eigg on the starboard bow;
Glory of youth glowed in his soul:
Where is that glory now?

Sing me a song of a lad that is gone,
Say, could that lad be I?
Merry of soul he sailed on a day
Over the sea to Skye.

Give me again all that was there,
Give me the sun that shone!
Give me the eyes, give me the soul,
Give me the lad that's gone!

Sing me a song of a lad that is gone,
Say, could that lad be I?
Merry of soul he sailed on a day
Over the sea to Skye.

Billow and breeze, islands and seas,
Mountains of rain and sun,
All that was good, all that was fair,
All that was me is gone.

Robert Louis Stevenson

Dance to your daddy

Dance to your daddy,
    My little babby,
Dance to your daddy,
    My little lamb.

You shall have a fishy
    In a little dishy,
You shall have a fishy
    When the boat comes in.

                                        Anonymous

Longing

The small blue boat
Tugs on its rope,
Dying to be free,
While fins
And tins
And twigs
And sprigs
And tide
And glide
And eels
And keels
And whirls
And swirls
And sticks
And slicks
And litter
And glitter
And tails
And sails
And crates
And spates
And floats
And boats
And sweepings from the quay
Pass
Bobbing, prancing,
Ducking, dancing
Downstream to the sea.

                                        Richard Edwards

Sea-fever

I must down to the seas again, to the lonely sea and the sky,
And all I ask is a tall ship and a star to steer her by,
And the wheel's kick and the wind's song and the white sail's shaking,
And a grey mist on the sea's face and a grey dawn breaking.

I must down to the seas again, for the call of the running tide
Is a wild call and a clear call that may not be denied;
And all I ask is a windy day with the white clouds flying,
And the flung spray and the blown spume, and the sea-gulls crying.

I must down to the seas again, to the vagrant gypsy life,
To the gull's way and the whale's way
where the wind's like a whetted knife;
And all I ask is a merry yarn from a laughing fellow-rover,
And quiet sleep and a sweet dream when the long trick's over.

John Masefield

The Owl and the Pussy-Cat

The Owl and the Pussy-Cat went to sea
In a beautiful pea-green boat.
They took some honey, and plenty of money,
Wrapped up in a five-pound note.
The Owl looked up to the stars above,
And sang to a small guitar,
'O lovely Pussy! O Pussy, my love,
What a beautiful Pussy you are,
You are!
What a beautiful Pussy you are!'

Pussy said to the Owl, 'You elegant fowl,
How charmingly sweet you sing!
Oh! Let us be married! too long we have tarried:
But what shall we do for a ring?'
They sailed away for a year and a day,
To the land where the Bong-tree grows;
And there in a wood a Piggy-wig stood,
With a ring at the end of his nose,
His nose,
With a ring at the end of his nose.

'Dear Pig, are you willing to sell for one shilling
Your ring?' Said the Piggy, 'I will.'
So they took it away, and were married next day
By the Turkey who lives on the hill.
They dined on mince, and slices of quince,
Which they ate with a runcible spoon;
And hand in hand, on the edge of the sand,
They danced by the light of the moon,
The moon,
They danced by the light of the moon.

Edward Lear

Four pirates

1. *Pebble-eye Jones*
Captain Jones of the *Golden Locket*
lost an eye while off Cape Crockett,
stuffed a pebble in the socket.

Liked his prisoners to walk the plank
and giggled as they fell...and sank.
Grew fat and rich – a walking bank.

2. *Peg-leg*
Each day old Peg sat on the quay
and stretched out straight his wooden knee,
told tales of monsters of the sea.

The cabin boys turned pale and stark
when told how, swimming after dark,
Peg lost his leg to a hungry shark.

3. *Pinkbeard*
This pirate had no beard at all,
pink chin smooth as a marble hall
and voice clear as a robin's call.

This pirate strange with big brown eyes
and flowing hair and sudden sighs.
The truth? A woman...in disguise!

4. *Captain Death*
He bossed a ship of forty guns.
He called his crew 'bloodthirsty sons';
they fought and swore like savage Huns.

Grim Captain Death strode decks of teak.
He sank a treasure ship each week,
and when he calls...*you'll* hear him speak.

Wes Magee

The pirates' song

Fifteen men on the Dead Man's Chest –
   Yo-ho-ho, and a bottle of rum!
Drink and the devil had done for the rest –
   Yo-ho-ho, and a bottle of rum!

Robert Louis Stevenson

The wonders of the mighty deep

Behold the wonders of the mighty deep,
Where crabs and lobsters learn to creep,
And little fishes learn to swim,
And clumsy sailors tumble in.

Anonymous

A sea-serpent

A sea-serpent saw a big tanker,
Bit a hole in her side and then sank her.
   It swallowed the crew
   In a minute or two,
And then picked its teeth with the anchor.

Anonymous

It

It was huge,
It was enormous,
It came dripping from the sea;
It wobbled down the promenade,
It passed quite close to me!
It ruined all the flower-beds,
It upset an ice-cream stall,
It was like a giant jellyfish and
It had no eyes at all.
It cleared the paddling pool of kids,
Its feelers swung and swayed,
It seemed to like the fruit machines as
It oozed through the arcade.
It burst the turnstile on the pier as
It squeezed its grey mass through,
It left a horrid track behind –
It was like a trail of glue.
It reached the pier's end railings and
It forced them till they split.
It flopped back down into the sea and
It vanished. That was It.

Eric Finney

The mermaid

A mermaid sat
On a sandy rock,
And her eyes gleamed soft and green.
'Come with me,' she called,
'And I'll take you away
To the land beneath the sea.'

'We'll ride on a dolphin,
We'll tickle a whale,
Eat seaweed cake for our tea.'
And she held out her hand
As she dived through the waves,
'Come with me
          Come with me
                    Come with me.'

Theresa Heine

from...The mermaid

Who would be
A mermaid fair,
Singing alone,
Combing her hair
Under the sea,
In a golden curl
With a comb of pearl,
On a throne?

from...The merman

Who would be
A merman bold,
Sitting alone,
Singing alone
Under the sea,
With a crown of gold,
On a throne?

Alfred, Lord Tennyson

The song of the whale

Heaving mountain in the sea,
Whale, I heard you
Grieving.

Great whale, crying for your life,
Crying for your kind, I knew
How we would use
Your dying:

Lipstick for our painted faces,
Polish for our shoes.

Tumbling mountain in the sea,
Whale, I heard you
Calling.

Bird-high notes, keening, soaring:
At their edge a tiny drum
Like a heart-beat.

We would make you
Dumb.

In the forest of the sea,
Whale, I heard you
Singing,

Singing to your kind.
We'd never let you be.
Instead of life we choose

Lipstick for our painted faces,
Polish for our shoes.

Kit Wright

The Kraken

Below the thunders of the upper deep;
Far, far beneath in the abysmal sea,
His ancient, dreamless, uninvaded sleep,
The Kraken sleepeth: faintest sunlights flee
Above his shadowy sides: above him swell
Huge sponges of millennial growth and height;
And far away into the sickly light,
From many a wondrous grot and secret cell
Unnumber'd and enormous polypi
Winnow with giant arms the slumbering green.
There hath he lain for ages and will lie
Battening upon huge seaworms in his sleep,
Until the latter fire shall heat the deep;
Then once by men and angels to be seen,
In roaring he shall rise and on the surface die.

Alfred, Lord Tennyson

Full fathom five

Full fathom five thy father lies;
Of his bones are coral made,
Those are pearls that were his eyes;
Nothing of him that doth fade
But doth suffer a sea-change
Into something rich and strange.
Sea-nymphs hourly ring his knell:
                          Ding-dong.
Hark, now I hear them, – Ding-dong bell.

William Shakespeare

UP AND AWAY

High life

My home is on the eighty-ninth floor.
I live above the storms.

My windows are the cockpit
of an airplane that never flies.

The builders thought they were smart
but the wind is smarter

and I grow dizzy and weak
as I watch the water in my sink

flop back and forth
as we blow to and fro.

I grab the towel rack
to steady myself.

A wispy cloud
crashes through my livingroom wall.

I scream over the phone
'what's the weather like down there?'

Julie O'Callaghan

Facts about air

Scientists say
That air consists
Of about 78 per cent nitrogen
And 21 per cent oxygen,
Plus some carbon dioxide
And small amounts
Of the rare gases
– helium, argon and neon.

These are facts, I know.
But I also know
That when I go outside
On a spring morning
The air tastes as crisp
As a fresh lettuce
And that when I sit
On the patio
On a summer evening
The cool night air
Brushes my cheeks like a feather.

John Foster

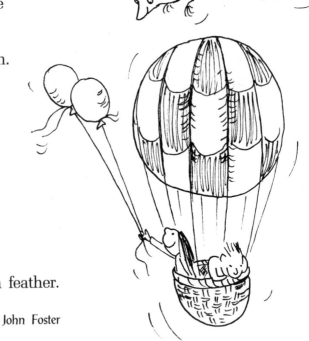

Summer dreams

Birds and bees and butterflies,
Big balloons in clear, blue skies,
Drifting dandelion seeds,
Floating, flying in the breeze.

Wendy Larmont

Clouds

Clouds
The white shrouds
Outspread
Overhead
Of ships under sail
Driven by the gale...

Icebergs of the sky
Mountainously high...
Suds
of foam
on an airy stream...
Piled-up helpings
of soft
ice-cream...

Castles in the air...
The wind's long hair...
The
gigantic
form
of
the thunderstorm...

Curtains drawn on the Sun at noon
or at midnight on the Moon...

Arctic archipelago
of islands under snow...

Banners unfurled

Above the world...

Stanley Cook

Windways

Can you *see* the wind?
No; but he is there,
bending, brushing, smoothing grass,
combing earth's wild hair.

Can you *hear* the wind?
Yes; he pants through trees;
whispers, whines beneath your door:
Can I come in, please?

Can you *smell* the wind?
No; but if you choose,
in his breath you'll smell the smoke
of Autumn barbecues.

Can you *feel* the wind?
Yes; you'll feel his breath
chilling cheeks and chin and lips,
chasing through your teeth.

Can you *taste* the wind?
Only when, on dark December nights,
the chestnut seller roasts his wares
beneath the Christmas lights...

Breathe in deeply: you will find
you can almost taste the wind.

Judith Nicholls

Who has seen the wind?

Who has seen the wind?
Neither I nor you:
But when the leaves hang trembling
The wind is passing through.

Who has seen the wind?
Neither you nor I:
But when the trees bow down their heads
The wind is passing by.

Christina Rossetti

Storm

Close the door and window,
    pull the curtains to.
Lightning wipes the sky white
    and frightens me and you.
For once weather's everything,
    everything we do.

Sit by the fire's flicker.
    The hurricane just threw
a wild gust against the glass –
    the garden gate's askew.
For once weather's everything,
    everything we do.

A wild sound. A smaller one:
    a sad beseeching mew.
I edge the front door open
    and the cat comes through.
For once weather's everything,
    everything we do.

Fred Sedgwick

Windy nights

Whenever the moon and stars are set,
    Whenever the wind is high,
All night long in the dark and wet,
    A man goes riding by.
Late in the night when the fires are out,
Why does he gallop and gallop about?

Whenever the trees are crying aloud,
    And ships are tossed at sea,
By, on the highway, low and loud,
    By at the gallop goes he.
By at the gallop he goes, and then
By he comes back at the gallop again.

Robert Louis Stevenson

Blow, wind, blow

Blow, wind, blow!
Go, windmill, go!
That the miller may grind the corn;
That the baker may take it,
And into bread bake it,
And bring to us
In the morn.

Anonymous

Dragonfly

I am a small iridescent twig,
Silver-wrapped like a thin sweet.
A catch-sun, though you'll not catch me,
Too quick as I skim the waters I came from.
When I pause on a reed or lily's landing pad
I'm watching you as you marvel.
You look again: I've gone.

John Cotton

from...Morning after a storm

There was a roaring in the wind all night;
The rain came heavily and fell in floods;
But now the sun is rising calm and bright.
The birds are singing in the distant woods;
Over his own sweet voice the stock-dove broods.
The jay makes answer as the magpie chatters;
And all the air is filled with pleasant noise of waters.

William Wordsworth

Cobweb morning

On a Monday morning
We do spellings and Maths.
And silent reading.

But on the Monday
After the frost
We went straight outside.

Cobwebs hung in the cold air,
Everywhere.
All around the playground,
They clothed the trees,
Dressed every bush
In veils of fine white lace.

Each web,
A wheel of patient spinning.
Each spider,
Hidden,
Waiting.

Inside,
We worked all morning
To capture the outside.

Now
In our patterns and poems
We remember
The cobweb morning.

June Crebbin

The eagle

He clasps the crag with crooked hands;
Close to the sun in lonely lands,
Ringed with the azure world, he stands.

The wrinkled sea beneath him crawls;
He watches from his mountain walls,
And like a thunderbolt he falls.

Alfred, Lord Tennyson

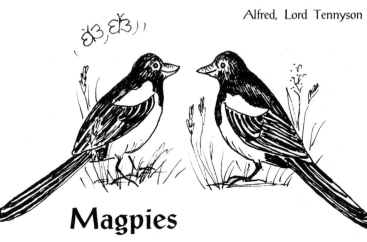

Magpies

One for sorrow,
Two for joy,
Three for a kiss,
Four for a boy,
Five for silver,
Six for gold,
Seven for a secret
never to be told,
Eight for a letter
from over the sea,
Nine for a lover
as true as can be.

Anonymous

Robin-a-Bobbin

Robin-a-Bobbin
He bent his bow,
Shot at a pigeon
And killed a crow.
Shot at another
And killed his own brother,
Did Robin-a-Bobbin
When he bent his bow.

Anonymous

The ptarmigan

The ptarmigan is strange,
The strangest bird to see;
Never sits on ptelephone poles
Or roosts up in a ptree.
But the way she ptakes pto spelling
Is the strangest pthing pto me.

Anonymous

The birdwatcher's first notebook

Monday – to the reservoir,
Real beginner's luck,
Saw a quack-quack-quacking thing,
Think it was a...grebe.

Tuesday – to the farmyard,
Only mud, but then
Saw a cluck-cluck-clucking thing,
Think it was a...partridge.

Wednesday – out at midnight,
Tom-cats on the prowl,
Heard a twit-twit-twooing thing,
Think it was a...nightingale.

Thursday – to the seaside,
Weather grey and dull,
Saw a big white wailing thing,
Think it was a...spoonbill.

Friday – brown bird on the lawn,
Outside in a rush,
Saw a worm tug-tugging thing,
Think it was a...pipit.

Saturday – to the heathery moor,
Scanned the sky and hark!
Heard a trill-trill-trilling thing,
Think it was a...curlew.

Sunday – tired of birdwatching,
Made a bamboo wicket,
Asked some friends round, cadged a bat,
Had a game of...football.

Richard Edwards

from...The owl

When cats run home and light is come,
And dew is cold upon the ground,
And the far-off stream is dumb,
And the whirring sail goes round,
And the whirring sail goes round;
Alone and warming his five wits,
The white owl in the belfry sits.

Alfred, Lord Tennyson

Aeroplane

Like a knife-blade slicing the sky in two,
a vapour cuts cleanly through the blue;
the only white in a cloudless day
spreads slowly as heaven's edges fray,
tearing like silk;
azure streaked with milk.

And only later, when the steel bird
is out of sight, is an engine heard.

Celia Warren

The glider

T_wi_st_in_g

and t
u
r
n
i
n
g,

Gliding with ease –

s
p
i
n
n
i
n
g,

beginning

To float with the breeze;

Lazily,

c R e 𝒵i ₗ y

hung

in the air –

Long way up -

– dn ʎɐʍ ƃuoɹ𝖶

And never a care!

Trevor Harvey

Balloon fiesta

Apostrophes of the air,
they soar like bubbles
making speech marks
in the evening sky.

Their colours blossom
into zigzags and spirals
as they dip down, skimming
across backlit fields.

When dragon-fires roar,
they rise, punctuating
the sky in a matrix
of disappearing dots...

Moira Andrew

Balloons!

A balloon
is a wild
space animal,

restless pet
who bumps and butts
its head
on the cage walls
of a room –

bursts with a bellow,
or escapes slowly
with sighs
leaving a limp skin.

Balloons
on the street
fidget
in fresh air,
strain
at their string
leashes.

If you loose
a balloon,
it bolts home
for the moon.

Judith Thurman

Hot air balloon

Here be dragons...Old maps bred them, just too far
away to catch or tame, of course. But what comes here:

over the trees with a gravelly huff, half sigh, half roar,
and a prickle of flame? I drop my book and stare

as it shoulders the sun aside. It settles, slow
as an eclipse, a candy-striped Big Top, hushed now

but for a creak of tackle, wind-hum in the wires...
The awning sags; its crate of precious wares,

half tiger cage, half laundry basket, thuds down,
spilling a figure out like dice across the lawn.

He finds his feet, dusts his greatcoat, wraps his scarf
twice round, squares his sideburns and his sad moustache,

and strides towards me, tipsy-brisk, as if uncertain
which of us is Stanley, which is Dr. Livingstone.

He does not have to speak. I know where he has been –
over glassy deserts, jungles steaming in the sun,

peevish oceans, to the limits, to the outer regions
where the maps go blank, and men dream dragons,

anything, to fill the awful void of Do-Not-Know
that drifts in, endless, indescribable, like snow.

Philip Gross

Song of the pilots in World War II

When you're seven miles up in the heavens
    And that's a heck of a lonely spot,
And it's 50 degrees below zero,
    Which isn't exactly hot,
When you're frozen as blue as your Spitfire,
    And you're scared a Mosquito pink,
When you're thousands of miles from nowhere,
    And there's nothing below but the drink –
It's then you will see the gremlins,
    Green and gamboge and gold,
Male and female and neuter,
    Gremlins both young and old.

White ones'll wiggle your wing-tips,
    Male ones'll muddle your maps,
Green ones'll guzzle your glycol,
    Females will flutter your flaps,
Pink ones will perch on your perspex,
    And dance pirouettes on your prop.
There's one spherical middle-aged gremlin
    Who spins on your stick like a top.
They'll freeze up your camera shutters,
    They'll bite through your aileron wires,
They'll cause your whole tail to flutter,
    They'll insert toasting forks in your tyres.

Anonymous

Countdown

'Dial,' said the poster,
'6 5 4 3 2 1
for an unforgettable experience.'

I lifted the receiver,
put money
in the slot, dialled
the number.

The phone box
TOOK OFF!

Thundering flames
shot me upwards
into the circle
of a sapphire sky;

above trees, houses,
traffic, people,
beyond birds,
beyond clouds;

into the clear
blue stratosphere
without a ticket –
I'm still up here,

leaving Earth
at the speed of light,
sending this message
by satellite.

Irene Rawnsley

Rocket launch

Flaring, flaming, red-orange-yellow,
Blinding steam billowing, yellow-grey-white,
Metal shining, nose-cone probing
Into the distance, into the night.

Clanging, spinning, climbing, fading,
Smaller and smaller, gaining height,
Daylight, twilight, starlight, moonlight,
Into orbit, an everlasting flight.

Anne English

Space vehicle

Space vehicle:
One of a fleet of nine.
This one, though,
Is yours and mine.

Eric Finney

I want to be an astronaut

I want to be an astronaut
And shoot off into space;
I want to float like a silver bird
Above the human race.

I want to ride a rocket,
Computerised (with lights);
I want to go beyond the stars
I've seen on winter nights.

I want the Earth to watch me
On their TV screens;
I want them all to see me go
Amongst fantastic scenes.

I want to be an astronaut
And go to Saturn soon;
I want to step down on to Mars
And the dark side of the Moon.

I want to spend my holidays
In a rocket that I'll fly;
I want to be an astronaut
Who waves our world goodbye.

I want to see the other worlds
And boys that aren't like me;
I want to see the strangest lands
And still be home for tea.

Peter Thabit Jones

Space food

Poor old spacemen
When they want to eat
Have to squeeze a toothpaste tube
Full of veg. and meat.

Anita Marie Sackett

Is the Moon tired?

Is the Moon tired? She looks so pale
Within her misty veil;
She scales the sky from east to west,
And takes no rest.

Before the coming of the night
The moon shows papery white;
Before the dawning of the day,
She fades away.

Christina Rossetti

The moon

The moon meanders through the night
Like a lollipop on a galactic flight,
And round her gossip with Venus and Mars
Hundreds and thousands of peppermint stars.

Theresa Heine

Starlight

Starlight,
Starbright.
First star I see tonight,
I wish I may,
I wish I might,
Have this wish I wish tonight.

Anonymous

Escape at bedtime

The lights from the parlour and kitchen shone out
    Through the blinds and the windows and bars;
And high overhead and all moving about,
    There were thousands of millions of stars.
There ne'er were such thousands of leaves on a tree,
    Nor of people in church or the park,
As the crowds of the stars that looked down upon me,
    And that glittered and winked in the dark.

The Dog, and the Plough, and the Hunter, and all,
    And the star of the sailor, and Mars,
These shone in the sky, and the pail by the wall
    Would be half full of water and stars.
They saw me at last, and they chased me with cries,
    And they soon had me packed into bed;
But the glory kept shining and bright in my eyes,
    And the stars going round in my head.

Robert Louis Stevenson

Home fires

At the back of my house
The sun expires
In a Wild West show
Full of dying fires.

At the front of my house
On windy nights
Trees throw up their arms
By the one street light.

And there in my bedroom
I try to sleep
While shadow flames dance
And flicker and creep.

Carol Coiffait

Darkness

Darkness is heavy
    it falls
        drops
            landing on me like a heavy quilt.

Darkness is frightening
    it stirs
        fears
            whispering to me in the night.

Marnie Francis

Storm at bedtime

Owls hoot,
thunder rolls;
doors bang,
wind howls.

Curtain sways,
shadows grow;
heart thumps...
Sleep? No!

Creaking stairs,
rustling trees;
Help, Mum,
COME, PLEASE!

Judith Nicholls

Ghosts

That's right. Sit down and talk to me.
What do you want to talk about?

Ghosts. You were saying that you believe in them.
Yes, they exist, without a doubt.

What, bony white nightmares that rattle and glow?
No, just spirits that come and go.

I've never heard such a load of rubbish.
Never mind, one day you'll know.

What makes you so sure?

I said:
What makes you so sure?

Hey,
Where did you go?

Kit Wright

The man who wasn't there

Yesterday upon the stair
I met a man who wasn't there;
He wasn't there again today,
I wish, I wish he'd go away.

I've seen his shapeless shadow-coat
Beneath the stairway, hanging about;
And outside, muffled in a cloak
The same colour as the dark;

I've seen him in a black, black suit
Shaking, under the broken light;
I've seen him swim across the floor
And disappear beneath the door;

And once, I almost heard his breath
Behind me, running up the path:
Inside, he leant against the wall,
And turned...and was no one at all.

Yesterday upon the stair,
I met a man who wasn't there;
He wasn't there again today,
I wish, I wish, he'd go away.

Brian Lee

House ghosts

Airing cupboard ghosts
hold music practices
inside the water tank.

Television ghosts
poke crooked fingers
across your favourite programme.

Chimney ghosts
sing one-note songs
over and over in owly voices.

Vacuum-cleaner ghosts
roar and the dust obeys them,
into the bag.

But the worst ghost
hides under your bed at night.

He makes no noise at all.

Irene Rawnsley

The longest journey in the world

'Last one in bed
has to switch out the light.'
It's just the same every night.
There's a race.
I'm ripping off my trousers and shirt,
he's kicking off his shoes and socks.

'My sleeve's stuck.'
'This button's too big for its button-hole.'
'Have you hidden my pyjamas?'
'Keep your hands off mine.'

If you win
you get where it's safe
before the darkness comes –
but if you lose
if you're last
you know what you've got coming up is
    the journey from the light switch to your bed.
It's the Longest Journey in the World.

'You're last tonight,' my brother says.
And he's right.

There is nowhere so dark
as that room in the moment
after I've switched out the light.

There is nowhere so full of dangerous things,
things that love dark places,
things that breathe only when you breathe
and hold their breath when I hold mine.

cont...

cont...

So I have to say:
'I'm not scared.'
That face, grinning in the pattern on the wall,
isn't a face –
'I'm not scared.'
That prickle on the back of my neck
is only the label on my pyjama jacket –
'I'm not scared.'
That moaning-moaning is nothing
but water in a pipe –
'I'm not scared.'

Everything's going to be just fine
as soon as I get into that bed of mine.
Such a terrible shame
it's always the same
it takes so long
it takes so long
it takes so long
to get there.

From the light switch
to my bed
it's the Longest Journey in the World.

Michael Rosen

PEOPLE, PEOPLE, PEOPLE

What has happened to Lulu?

What has happened to Lulu, mother?
What has happened to Lu?
There's nothing in her bed but an old rag-doll
And by its side a shoe.

Why is her window wide, mother,
The curtain flapping free,
And only a circle on the dusty shelf
Where her money-box used to be?

Why do you turn your head, mother,
And why do the tear-drops fall?
And why do you crumple that note on the fire
And say it is nothing at all?

I woke to voices late last night,
I heard an engine roar.
Why do you tell me the things I heard
Were a dream and nothing more?

I heard somebody cry, mother,
In anger or in pain,
But now I ask you why, mother,
You say it was a gust of rain.

Why do you wander about as though
You don't know what to do?
What has happened to Lulu, mother?
What has happened to Lu?

Charles Causley

United we stand

'Your brother's a *menace*.'
'He's not.'
'Your brother's a *nuisance*.'
'What rot!'

'Your brother's a *zombie*.'
'Not true.'
'He's a walking *disaster*.'
'Like you!'

We may have our quarrels
But on *this* we agree –
I stand up for my brother
And he stands up for me!

Trevor Harvey

Tickling

He giggles and squeaks,
And wriggles and cries,
And curls and rolls,
And screws up his eyes,
And squirms and squeals,
And shouts and yells,
And screeches and begs,
And bangs his legs,
Till mum puts her head
Round the door and says,
'Stop tickling your brother!'

Theresa Heine

Grandma

'I remember
when I could sunfill my face
with fields of cowslips.'

Her eyes glazed
As she reflected her girlhood.
And I longed to butter my chin
With the wild flowers of her youth.

Later that year
We took her to hidden
Country depths
And by the roadside,
Fullcreamed and flourishing,
The cowlips bunched
On untouched banks.

'See, see,' she cried,
'That's *just* how it used to be!'

Anita Marie Sackett

A cupboard in my Grandfather's house

A cupboard,
In my Grandfather's house,
Where they kept the baby birds,
The chicks;
When they opened the door
Next to the cosy fire,
We children saw
And heard
A moving warm crowd of golden feathers.

Peter Thabit Jones

Photographs

Who's that figure standing there,
slim at the waist, shoulder-length hair?
That's your dad twenty years ago,
wouldn't think so now, though.

Who's that young girl skipping high,
caught against a sunny sky?
That's your mum some years ago,
looks a bit different now, though.

Who's that tall and lanky lad,
looks a little bit like dad?
That's his brother, Uncle Joe,
wouldn't know him now, though.

Who's that lady on the swing,
smiling and laughing at everything?
That's Auntie many years ago,
she doesn't smile much now, though.

Who's that tiny wrinkled baby,
mouth wide open, bawling loudly?
Oh come on now, surely you know,
you're still a noisy so and so!

Brian Moses

Big Aunt Flo'

Every Sunday afternoon
She visits us for tea
And weighs in somewhere between
A rhino and a flea.
(But closer to the rhino!)

Aunt Flo' tucks into doughnuts,
Eats fruit cake by the tin.
Her stomach makes strange noises
Just like my rude friend, Flynn.
(Sounds more like a goat, really!)

Then after tea she heads for
The best chair in the room
And crashes on the cushions
With one resounding boom.
(You'd think a door had slammed!)

Flo' sits on knitting needles
And snaps them with a crack.
She squashes dolls and jigsaws
Behind her massive back.
(And she doesn't feel a thing!)

But Aunt Flo' learned a lesson,
There's no doubt about that,
Last Sunday when she grabbed the chair
And sat down on our cat.
(Big Tom, a cat with a temper!)

The beast let out a wild yell
And dug his claws in...deep.
Poor Flo' clutched her huge behind
And gave a mighty leap.
(She almost reached the ceiling!)

So now at Sunday teatime
Jam doughnuts going spare,
Dad winks, and asks where Flo' is;
While Tom sleeps on *that* chair.
(And he's purring, the devil!)

Wes Magee

Cousin Lesley's see-through stomach

Cousin Lesley took a pill
That made her go invisible.
Perhaps this would have been all right
If everything was out of sight.

But all around her stomach swam
Half-digested bread and jam,
And no matter how she tried
She couldn't hide what was inside.

In the morning we often noted
How the toast and porridge floated,
And how unappetizing in the light
Was the curry from last night.

Some Gruyère had fallen victim
To her strange digestive system,
And there seemed a million ways
To digest old mayonnaise.

We were often fascinated
By the stuff left undigested,
A mish-mash of peas and jelly
Drifted round our cousin's belly.

Certain bits of Cornish pastie
Looked repugnant and quite nasty,
While the strawberries from last year
Were without the cream, I fear.

And at dinner, oh dear me!
What a disgusting sight to see
Chewed-up fish and cold brown tea
Where Cousin Lesley's tum should be.

Brian Patten

I know someone who can

I know someone who can
take a mouthful of custard and blow it
down their nose.
I know someone who can
make their ears wiggle.
I know someone who can
shake their cheeks so it sounds
like ducks quacking.
I know someone who can
throw peanuts in the air and catch them
in their mouth.
I know someone who can
balance a pile of 12 2p pieces on his elbow
and snatch his elbow from under them
and catch them.
I know someone who can
bend her thumb back to touch her wrist.
I know someone who can
crack his nose.
I know someone who can
say the alphabet backwards.
I know someone who can put their hands in
their armpits and blow raspberries.
I know someone who can
wiggle her little toe.
I know someone who can
lick the bottom of her chin.
I know someone who can
slide the top lip one way
and their bottom lip the other way,
and that someone is
ME.

Michael Rosen

Shocking

Prepare to be outraged,
Astounded, appalled:
Under their hairiness
Everyone's BALD!

And here's a fact
Even more shocking and rude:
Under their underclothes
Everyone's NUDE!

Eric Finney

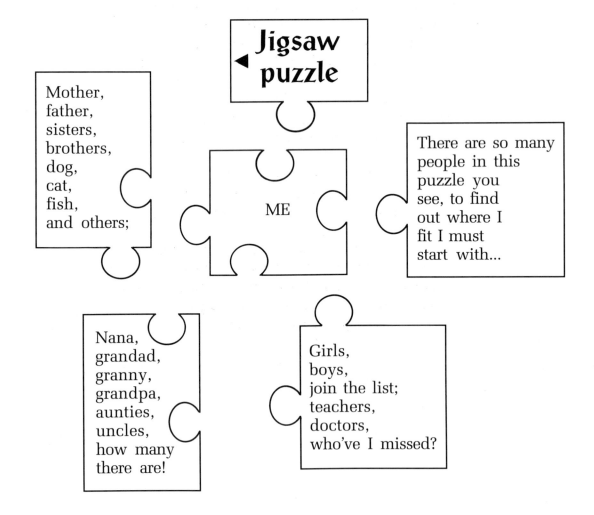

Jigsaw puzzle

Mother,
father,
sisters,
brothers,
dog,
cat,
fish,
and others;

ME

There are so many
people in this
puzzle you
see, to find
out where I
fit I must
start with...

Nana,
grandad,
granny,
grandpa,
aunties,
uncles,
how many
there are!

Girls,
boys,
join the list;
teachers,
doctors,
who've I missed?

Laurelle Rond

One

Only one of me
and nobody can get a second one
from a photocopy machine.

Nobody has the fingerprints I have.
Nobody can cry my tears, or laugh my laugh
or have my expectancy when I wait.

But anybody can mimic my dance with my dog.
Anybody can howl how I sing out of tune.
And mirrors can show me multiplied
many times, say, dressed up in red
or dressed up in grey.

Nobody can get into my clothes for me
or feel my fall for me, or do my running.
Nobody hears my music for me, either.

I am just this one.
Nobody else makes the words
I shape with sound, when I talk.

But anybody can act how I stutter in a rage.
Anybody can copy echoes I make.
And mirrors can show me multiplied
many times, say, dressed up in green
or dressed up in blue.

James Berry

In one second

In one second I can –

Clap my hands
or
do handstands.

Pop my mouth
or
take one step south.

Blink my eyes
or
shrink in size.

Jump out of bed
or
pretend I'm dead.

Swallow a fly
or
say goodbye.

Turn a page
or
get in a rage.

Scratch an itch
or
start a twitch.

Swallow a sweet
or
tap my feet.

Collapse in a heap
or
just simply fall asleep.

Ian Souter

Treasure trove

I have a tin
to keep things in
underneath
my bedroom floor.

I put my finger
in the crack,
quietly lift
the floorboard back,

and there's my store,
safely hid
in a tin with roses
on the lid.

A few feathers
and a chicken's claw,
a big tooth
from a dinosaur,

the wrapper
from my Easter egg,
a Christmas robin
with one leg,

long hairs
from a horse's mane,
real pesetas
come from Spain,

three of my
operation stitches,
like spiders
wrapped in bandages,

a marble
full of dragon smoke,
flashing with fire
in the dark,

a magic pebble
round and white,
a sparkler left
from bonfire night.

Underneath
my bedroom floor
there's a treasure tin,
with my things in.

Irene Rawnsley

Knickers

Not wearing knickers,
not navy,
no more.

Want to wear silk ones
'cos cotton's
a bore.

Want to wear pink ones
with frills.
I adore

not wearing knickers,
not navy,
no more.

Gina Douthwaite

The best bed

The best bed's a single bed,
the best bed of all.
There's football posters all around
the bedroom wall.

There's piles and piles of Asterix books
and comics everywhere
and if you say the room's a mess
I don't care.

The best bed's a trampoline
and the best bed's a ship
where the sea's a carpet strewn with things,
a proper tip.

The best bed's where my mother comes
and kisses me, and all
the football players are smiling down
from my wall.

Fred Sedgwick

The girl in red stockings

Red stockings,
Red stockings,
Shoes tied up with silver;
A red rose
Upon my chest
And a gold ring on my finger.

Anonymous

80

When I am old and 80
in the year twenty, twenty-three

I'll wear my hair in ringlets,
wear purple breeches to the knee.

I'll race around on roller skates
and whistle in the park,

sing songs along the High Street
and *never* fear the dark.

I'll drive a bus up Cot Hill
and learn to ride a bike.

And when I'm feeling crabbity
blow raspberries through a mic.

So when my problems grow too big
I'll laugh and slap my knee

And imagine when I'm 80
In the year twenty, twenty-three.

Kay Cornish

Catherine wheel

I used to go around with her all the time until we had this row and she went off with Tracy so that left me to tag along with Wendy and Debs till they stopped speaking to each other and I couldn't choose between them when up comes Anyusha who'd fallen out with her friend Jackie and we went round together so that was that and that's why I'm going round with Catherine...

AGAIN

David Horner

Best friends

'Shall we have a fight?' asks Bill.
'Dunno,' says yawning John.
Arms about each other's necks
They amble slowly on.

Cynthia Mitchell

Today, in strong colours

Today, in strong colours,
I want you to welcome a visitor.
Give her
A purple wave
A bright red smile
A round of green applause
A royal blue handshake
And a yellow hello.
Place her firmly
On the palette of our friendship.

Sue Cowling

Jenny Hall

Jenny Hall
    she is so small,
a mouse could eat her,
    hat and all.

Anonymous

Mary and Sarah

Mary likes smooth things,
Things that glide:
Sleek skis swishing down a mountainside.

Sarah likes rough things,
Things that snatch:
Boats with barnacled bottoms, thatch.

Mary likes smooth things,
Things all mellow:
Milk, silk, runny honey, tunes on a cello.

Sarah likes rough things,
Things all troubly:
Crags, snags, bristles, thistles, fields left stubbly.

Mary says – polish,
Sarah says – rust,
Mary says – mayonnaise,
Sarah says – crust.

Sarah says – hedgehogs,
Mary says – seals,
Sarah says – sticklebacks,
Mary says – eels.

Give me, says Mary,
The slide of a stream,
The touch of a petal,
A bowl of ice-cream.

Give me, says Sarah,
The gales of a coast,
The husk of a chestnut,
A plate of burnt toast.

Mary and Sarah –
They'll never agree
Till peaches and coconuts
Grow on one tree.

Richard Edwards

Boy/girl story

I like her
    because she's sporty
    in a sparky sort of way.
She's good at rounders,
brill at cricket,
lets me kick in goals all day.

I like him
    because he's funny
    in a kindly sort of way.
He laughs at my jokes,
doesn't bully,
knows some super tricks to play.

I like the way
    she draws neat pictures
    full of detail, colours bright.
'Miss' says she writes the zaniest stories
although her spelling's not quite right.

I like the way
    he builds great models
    from junk and wire, action packed.
'Sir' says he has a gift for DT
although he *can* forget the facts.

I hope he asks *me*
    to the disco
    at the youth club, Sat'day night.
If he does
    the other girls
    will envy me,
think I'm all right.

I wonder if she'll
    watch the next match
    when I'm playing for the school.
If she does,
    the other lads
    might tease a bit,
but think I'm cool.

Jill Jesson

The new kid on the block

There's a new kid on the block,
and boy, that kid is tough,
that new kid punches hard,
that new kid plays real rough,
that new kid's big and strong,
with muscles everywhere,
that new kid tweaked my arm,
that new kid pulled my hair.

That new kid likes to fight,
and picks on all the guys,
that new kid scares me some,
(that new kid's twice my size),
that new kid stomped my toes,
that new kid swiped my ball,
that new kid's really bad,
I don't care for her at all.

Jack Prelutsky

An alphabet of horrible habits

A is for Albert
who makes lots of noise

B is for Bertha
who bullies the boys

C is for Cuthbert
who teases the cat

D is for Dilys
whose singing is flat

E is for Enid
who's never on time

F is for Freddy
who's covered in slime

G is for Gilbert
who never says thanks

H is for Hannah
who plans to rob banks

I is for Ivy
who slams the front door

J is for Jacob
whose jokes are a bore

K is for Kenneth
who won't wash his face

L is for Lucy
who cheats in a race

M is for Maurice
who gobbles his food

N is for Nora
who runs about nude

O is for Olive
who treads on your toes

P is for Percy
who *will* pick his nose

Q is for Queenie
who won't tell the truth

R is for Rupert
who's rather uncouth

S is for Sibyl
who bellows and bawls

T is for Thomas
who scribbles on walls

U is for Una
who fidgets too much

V is for Victor
who talks double Dutch

W is for Wilma
who won't wipe her feet

X is for Xerxes
who never is neat

Y is for Yorick
who's vain as can be

Z is for Zoe
who doesn't love me.

Colin West

Who is he?

I saw him again
in the wind and the
rain,
dog on a string,
bag full of things,
blue tattoos,
worn-out shoes,
flapping coat,
scarf at throat,
angry brows.
And no one knows
who he is
or where
he goes.

Carol Coiffait

A man in the wilderness

A man in the wilderness asked me,
'How many strawberries grow in the sea?'

I answered him, as I thought I should,
'As many red herrings as swim in the wood!'

Anonymous

Queen Nefertiti

Spin a coin, spin a coin,
    All fall down;
Queen Nefertiti
    Stalks through the town.

Over the pavements
    Her feet go clack.
Her legs are as tall
    As a chimney stack.

Her fingers flicker
    Like snakes in the air,
The walls split open
    At her green-eyed stare;

Her voice is thin
    As the ghosts of bees;
She will crumble your bones,
    She will make your blood freeze.

Spin a coin, spin a coin,
    All fall down;
Queen Nefertiti
    Stalks through the town.

Anonymous

Climbing boy

Ben climbed inside the chimneys
told to clean out all the soot,
    and those flues were black
    as a warlock's hat
and precarious underfoot.

A waif picked from the workhouse,
being five years old, and scared.
    He was light and slight
    as a widow's mite.
He knew nothing. No one cared.

At first afraid to clamber,
then his master lit some straw
    in the grate below
    so that Ben would know
the fear of burning more.

He scaled the crooked tunnels
with his brush, just sweeping blind.
    So by slow degrees,
    with his battered knees,
he became at last resigned.

At dawn he ate his gruel
and at night his loaf of bread.
    Daily sixteen hours
    in those nightmare towers
he just swept and cried and bled.

A grimy, ragged urchin,
he was one of many then.
    Countless half-pint slaves
    went to paupers' graves
too soon, brushed off, like Ben.

Jenny Morris

Hassan's fish 'n' chip shop

Chips steam
In yesterday's newspapers.

We gravy our fingers in broken pies.

His dark face smiles from behind the counter,
As his wife shakes a basket of cooking fish.

Vinegar and salt,
Golden sticks of spud.
Chips! Chips! Chips!

The hot smell of food brings a long queue.

Outside, we share a bottle of pop;
Street lamps come on and butter the pavements.

Peter Thabit Jones

King Arthur

When Good King Arthur ruled the land,
He was a goodly king;
He stole three sacks of barley meal
To make a bag-pudding.

A bag-pudding the Queen did bake,
And stuffed it full of plums,
And in it put great lumps of fat
As big as my two thumbs.

The King and Queen sat down to dine,
And all the court beside;
And what they could not eat that night
The Queen next morning fried.

Anonymous

Quickstep

Way down Geneva,
All along Vine,
Deeper than the snowdrift
Love's eyes shine:

Mary Lou's walking
In the winter time.

She's got

Red boots on, she's got
Red boots on,
Kicking up the winter
Till the winter's gone.

So

Go by Ontario,
Look down Main,
If you can't Mary Lou
Come back again:

Sweet light burning
In winter's flame.

She's got

Snow in her eyes, got
A tingle in her toes
And new red boots on
Wherever she goes.

So

All around Lake Street,
Up by St. Paul,
Quicker than the white wind
Love takes all:

Mary Lou's walking
In the big snow fall.

She's got

Red boots on, she's got
Red boots on,
Kicking up the winter
Till the winter's

gone.

Kit Wright

from... The song of Hiawatha

Swift of foot was Hiawatha;
He could shoot an arrow from him,
And run forward with such fleetness,
That the arrow fell behind him!
Strong of arm was Hiawatha;
He could shoot ten arrows upward,
Shoot them with such strength and swiftness,
That the tenth had left the bowstring
Ere the first to earth had fallen!
He had mittens, Minjekahwun,
Magic mittens made of deerskin;
When upon his hands he wore them,
He could smite the rocks asunder,
He could grind them into powder.
He had moccasins enchanted,
Magic moccasins of deerskin;
When he bound them round his ankles,
When upon his feet he tied them,
At each stride a mile he measured!

Henry Wadsworth Longfellow

from...The Pied Piper of Hamelin

'Come in!' – the Mayor cried, looking bigger:
And in did come the strangest figure!
His queer long coat from heel to head
Was half of yellow and half of red;
And he himself was tall and thin,
With sharp blue eyes, each like a pin,
And light loose hair, yet swarthy skin,
No tuft on cheek nor beard on chin,
But lips where smiles went out and in –
There was no guessing his kith or kin!
And nobody could enough admire
The tall man and his quaint attire:
Quoth one: 'It's as if my great-grandsire,
Starting up at Trump of Doom's tone,
Had walked this way from his painted tombstone!'

He advanced to the council-table:
And, 'Please your honours,' said he, 'I'm able
By means of a secret charm to draw
All creatures living beneath the sun,
That creep or swim or fly or run,
After me so as you never saw!
And I chiefly use my charm
On creatures that do people harm,
The mole and toad and newt and viper;
and people call me the Pied Piper.'
(And here they noticed round his neck
A scarf of red and yellow stripe,
To match with his coat of the selfsame check;
And at the scarf's end hung a pipe;
And his fingers, they noticed, were ever straying
As if impatient to be playing
Upon this pipe, as low it dangled
Over his vesture so old-fangled.)

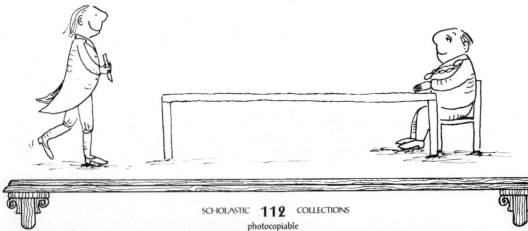

'Yet,' said he, 'poor piper that I am,
In Tartary I freed the Cham,
Last June, from his huge swarm of gnats;
I eased in Asia the Nizam
Of a monstrous brood of vampire-bats;
And, as for what your brain bewilders,
If I can rid your town of rats,
Will you give me a thousand guilders?'
'One? Fifty thousand!' – was the exclamation
Of the astonished Mayor and Corporation.

Into the street the Piper stept,
Smiling first a little smile,
As if he knew what magic slept
In his quiet pipe the while;
Then, like a musical adept,
To blow the pipe his lips he wrinkled,
And green and blue his sharp eyes twinkled
Like a candle-flame where salt is sprinkled;
And ere three shrill notes the pipe uttered,
You heard as if an army muttered;
And the muttering grew to a grumbling;
And the grumbling grew to a mighty rumbling;
And out the houses the rats came tumbling.
Great rats, small rats, lean rats, brawny rats,
Brown rats, black rats, grey rats, tawny rats,
Grave old plodders, gay young friskers,
Fathers, mothers, uncles, cousins,
Cocking tails and pricking whiskers,
Families by tens and dozens,
Brothers, sisters, husbands, wives –
Followed the Piper for their lives.

Robert Browning

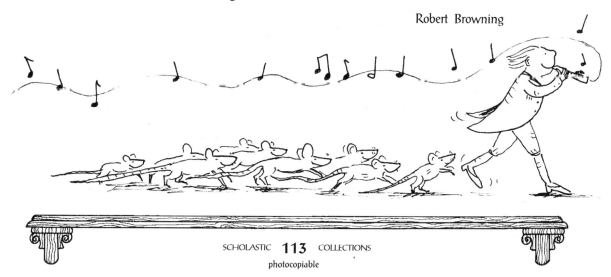

Some people in other lands

Some people in other lands
Hold begging bowls in their hands;

They have no drinks, they have no bread:
The sun burns hope inside each head.

Let's close our eyes, let's link our hands
And think of those in other lands.

Peter Thabit Jones

Two boys crying

Across the world
Two boys are crying,
Both wanting more
And tired of trying.

The first boy wants a mountain bike
And blames his mum for being mean;
Had enough of the daily hike,
He's desperate to be part of the scene.
All day long
The wanting burns strong.
All the night
The wanting burns bright.
So little to ask,
Bikes are everywhere;
Oh, why is life so unfair?

The second boy wants something to eat
But is too weak to place the blame.
His mother weeps, helpless, dead-beat,
While his father hangs his head in shame.
All day long
The hunger burns strong.
All the night
The hunger burns bright.
So little to ask,
Food is everywhere;
Oh, why is life so unfair?

Across the world
Two boys are crying,
One's full of life,
The other is dying.

Ray Mather

THE MODERN WORLD

Song of the Victorian mine

Shut six men in a metal cage –
    Wind them down, wind them down.
Drop them in a dismal pit –
    Down in the mine,
    Deep in the mine,
    Dark in the mine all day.

Back the pony up to the cage –
    Wind him down, wind him down.
Trip him up and make him sit –
    Down in the mine,
    Deep in the mine,
    Dark in the mine all day.

Load the ore in the metal cage –
    Wind it down, wind it down.
Waterlogged and candlelit –
    Down in the mine,
    Deep in the mine,
    Dark in the mine all day.

Bring the canary in his cage –
    Wind him down, wind him down.
He'll die first if the air's not fit –
    Down in the mine,
    Deep in the mine,
    Dark in the mine all day.

Thirty thousand times in the cage –
    Wind me down, wind me down.
Fill my lungs with grime and grit –
    Down in the mine,
    Deep in the mine,
    Dark in the mine all day.

Sue Cowling

Flint

An emerald is as green as grass,
    A ruby red as blood;
A sapphire shines as blue as heaven;
    A flint lies in the mud.

A diamond is a brilliant stone,
    To catch the world's desire;
An opal holds a fiery spark;
    But a flint holds fire.

Christina Rossetti

Firelight

Last night
as flames curled round my coal
I thought I saw
a million years ago
a forest fall.

Judith Nicholls

Coal

Black
diamonds,
Hard earned.
Flames licking,
Soon burned.

Wendy Larmont

Fire down below

Fire in the galley,
Fire down below;
It's fetch a bucket of water, girls,
There's fire down below.
    'Fire! Fire!' Fire down below,
It's fetch a bucket of water, girls,
There's fire down below.

Fire in the windlass,
Fire down below;
It's fetch a bucket of water, boys,
There's fire down below.
    'Fire! Fire!' Fire down below,
It's fetch a bucket of water, boys,
There's fire down below.

Fire up aloft,
And fire down below;
It's fetch a bucket of water, all,
There's fire down below.
    'Fire! Fire!' Fire down below,
It's fetch a bucket of water, all,
There's fire down below.

Anonymous

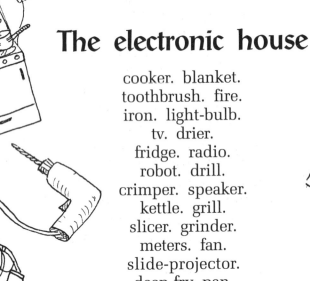

The electronic house

cooker. blanket.
toothbrush. fire.
iron. light-bulb.
tv. drier.
fridge. radio.
robot. drill.
crimper. speaker.
kettle. grill.
slicer. grinder.
meters. fan.
slide-projector.
deep-fry pan.
vacuum-cleaner.
fuses. shocks.
freezer. shaver.
junction box.
water heater.
Christmas lamps.
knife. recorder.
cables. amps.
door chimes. organ.
infra red.
guitar. video.
sunlamp bed.
synthesizer.
night light glow.
cultivator.
stereo.
calculator.
metronome.
toaster. Teasmade!
ohm, sweet, ohm.

Wes Magee

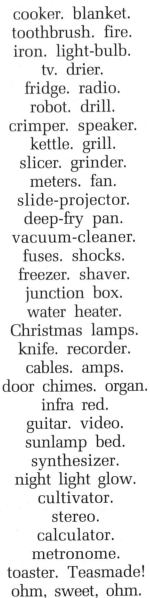

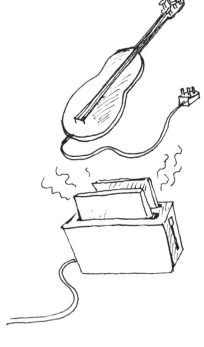

Electric energy

One flicked finger,
one clicked switch
and on.
GRRRRRRRRRRRRRR!
The food mixer growls
as electricity suddenly pulses
into its still white body
and shocks it awake.
From its socket mouth
an electric current
is pumping life into the very heart of the machine.
For three explosive minutes
the food mixer's plastic body
proudly swells as it announces
its awakening to the kitchen
in a full-throated way.
But all too quickly
the life blood of energy is cut
and its body shakingly shudders to a halt.
One flicked finger,
one clicked switch
and off.

Ian Souter

Electrickiller

There is a demon who lives in the wire.
He spits bright sparks and he breathes liquid fire.
If you shake his hand he will shock you to death,
No shadow of doubt, he'll steal all your breath.

Your forehead will sweat and your mouth will be dry.
Your hair will stand straight and your eyeballs will fry.
You'll burn to a crisp in a second or two.
End of this warning...end also of you!

Ian Larmont

Power cut

A storm swaggered out of the night
like an evil creature looking for a fight.
It wrapped its arms around our home
and spoke with a low and frightful moan.

Mum got up at half past three,
went downstairs and made cups of tea.
Soon after that the lights went out.
'Mum, come quick,' I heard myself shout.

'I don't like it, Mum, everything's gone black.
What's happened, Mum, are we under attack?'
'Don't worry,' she said, 'there'll be light again soon.
I'll bring you a candle to brighten your room.'

But at breakfast time there was still no power,
the house grew colder with each passing hour.
We had to have bread instead of toast,
we wouldn't be cooking our Sunday roast.

I couldn't play tapes or watch TV,
there was no hot water for making tea.
When Mum opened up the freezer door,
melted ice cream dripped on the floor.

We ate our tea by candlelight,
and carried our candles to bed that night.
Dad said, we'd be back to normal soon
as I fell asleep by the light of the moon.

Brian Moses

Fireflies

If
you collect
Enough fireflies
You could
Read secrets
Under your blanket
All night long

Zaro Weil

The fridge

Into the kitchen
At half-past three
And straight to the fridge –
What's in it for me?

A strawberry yoghurt?
A sticky Swiss Bun?
Oh an Angel Delight
Is my generous Mum!

So I open the door
But a breath of cold air
Is all that I find –
There's nothing there.

Now this really is not
How things should be
When you get home from school
At half-past three.

John Mole

Person power

Our car drinks lead-free petrol,
    it's a user-friendly fuel.
But I prefer to use my legs
    to get me safe to school.

Our house is all-electric,
    gas is what cookers like,
but I have lots of energy
    so I pedal my red bike.

The sun heats solar panels,
    the windmill likes the breeze,
the waves have awesome power
    but I need none of these.

Just give me my strong muscles
    a skateboard, bike or skates,
and I'll use person-power
    in the park to race my mates!

John Rice

The Hoover

The Hoover eats up anything –
Crisp crumbs, sweet wrappers, bits of string.

It grubs around behind the door,
Then snakes its way across the floor,

Gobbling up whatever's there –
Paper scraps, dust specks, strands of hair.

Beneath the table, under the chairs,
Along the hallway, up the stairs,

It swallows everything it can,
Like missing bits of Action Man!

Down the landing the Hoover crawls,
Sucking up dust beside the walls.

Crisp crumbs, sweet wrappers, bits of string –
The Hoover eats up anything.

Quick! Hurry up! Tidy the floor.
The Hoover's at your bedroom door!

John Foster

The Vault of Unwanted Inventions

The Vault of Unwanted Inventions
Is a sad and a funny old place,
Where the self-raising hat that has never been worn
Waits locked in its ebony case,
Where the yodelling scarecrow for farmers
And the pair of soundproof pyjamas,
The paint-spraying lamp-post for scaring off dogs,
The seven-houred clock and the litter-spike clogs
Lie patiently gathering dust,
Or slowly beginning to rust.

The Vault of Unwanted Inventions
Is a sad and a funny old room,
Where Moffat's magnetic suspenders for socks
Shine mournfully out of the gloom,
Where the plate with no bottom for slimmers
And the buoyant false teeth for non-swimmers,
The head-rest for roses beginning to droop,
The rhubarb detector, the scarf for cold soup,
The ant-bath, the sneezer, the four-legged tight,
The portable moon for a very dark night
And other things equally clever
Will probably languish for ever,
Preserved, with the best of intentions,
In the Vault of Unwanted Inventions.

Richard Edwards

The engineer

Let it rain!
Who cares?
I've a train
Upstairs,
With a brake
Which I make
From a string
Sort of thing,
Which works
In jerks,
'Cos it drops
In the spring,
Which stops
With the string,
And the wheels
All stick
So quick
That it feels
Like a thing
That you make
With a brake,
Not string...

So that's what I make,
When the day's all wet.
It's a good sort of brake
But it hasn't worked yet.

A.A. Milne

Road up

What's wrong with the road?
Why all this hush? –
They've given an anaesthetic
In the lunch-hour rush.

They've shaved off the tarmac
With a pneumatic drill,
And bandaged the traffic
To a dead standstill.

Surgeons in shirt-sleeves
Bend over the patient,
Intent on a major
Operation.

Don't dare sneeze!
Don't dare shout!
The road is having
Its appendix out.

Norman Nicholson

The digger's song

I'm a digger, a mechanical digger.
With my metal claws
I can scratch, I can scrape
Till I make the earth break.

I'm a digger, a mechanical digger.
With my metal jaws
I can bite, I can tear,
Ripping holes anywhere.

I'm a digger, a mechanical digger.
With my metal hands
I can scoop, I can lift.
Whole hills I can shift.

I'm a digger, a mechanical digger.
With my metal teeth
I can snatch, I can seize
Chunks of earth, roots of trees.

I'm a digger, a mechanical digger.
Where there's work to be done,
Send for me! I'm the one
Who shifts earth by the ton!

John Foster

The road sweeper machine

Sweeper, sweeper, clean-road-keeper,
swept my sister – wouldn't keep her!
Spat her from the suction hose
wearing only underclothes!

Gina Douthwaite

Tractor

Dressed in a coat of mud
and splattered with soil,
the farm tractor coughs and rasps
like a factory horn with a bad throat.

Huge tyres heave
the plough through the soggy field
churning the dark earth into
shapes like frozen waves.
Seagulls swoop and glide behind
like wild ribbons flowing free
in some great wind.

Up and down the valley, all day long –
the tractor never tires.
By evening its lights pierce
the gathering dusk
and its growl rolls over the fields
like a tumbling echo.
Slowly, the star-filled night
covers the countryside in a warm dark
that brings its own silent Plough.

John Rice

Metal fettle

The clank of a tank,
the chink of chains,
the tinkle of tins,
the rattle of trains.

The click of a clasp,
the clang of a bell,
the creak of a hinge,
the chime of a spell.

The shatter of cymbals,
the clash of swords,
the clatter of cutlery,
the twang of chords.

The ping of keys,
the song of a wheel,
the plink of pans,
the ring of steel.

John Rice

Machine riddle

I am the breaker of bones
I am the fouler of air
    Watch out for me once
    then twice
    then again...
Beware, oh beware!

I am the beast of sight
I can find my prey anywhere
    I can see what's to come
    what is now
    what is past...
Beware, oh beware!

And at night by my beacon sight
I follow a trail to my lair
    The gleaming spoor of
    blood-
        red
            eyes...
Beware, oh beware!

(answer: car)   Mick Gowar

The train to Glasgow

Here is the train to Glasgow.

Here is the driver,
Mr MacIver,
Who drove the train to Glasgow.

Here is the guard from Donibristle
Who waved his flag and blew his whistle
To tell the driver,
Mr MacIver,
To start the train to Glasgow.

Here is a boy called Donald MacBrain
Who came to the station to catch the train
But saw the guard from Donibristle
Wave his flag and blow his whistle
To tell the driver,
Mr MacIver,
To start the train to Glasgow.

Here is a guard, a kindly man
Who, at the last moment, hauled into the van
That fortunate boy called Donald MacBrain
Who came to the station to catch the train
But saw the guard from Donibristle
Wave his flag and blow his whistle
To tell the driver,
Mr MacIver,
To start the train to Glasgow.

Here are hens and here are cocks,
Clucking and crowing inside a box,
In charge of the guard, that kindly man
Who, at the last moment, hauled into the van
That fortunate boy called Donald Macbrain
Who came to the station to catch the train
But saw the guard from Donibristle
Wave his flag and blow his whistle
To tell the driver,
Mr MacIver,
To start the train to Glasgow.

cont...

Here is the train. It gave a jolt
Which loosened a catch and loosened a bolt,
And let out the hens and let out the cocks,
Clucking and crowing out of their box,
In charge of the guard, that kindly man
Who, at the last moment, hauled into the van
That fortunate boy called Donald MacBrain
Who came to the station to catch the train
But saw the guard from Donibristle
Wave his flag and blow his whistle
To tell the driver,
Mr MacIver,
To start the train to Glasgow.

The guard chased a hen and, missing it, fell.
The hens were all squawking, the cocks as well,
And unless you were there you haven't a notion
The flurry, the fuss, the noise and commotion
Caused by the train which gave a jolt
And loosened a catch and loosened a bolt
And let out the hens and let out the cocks,
Clucking and crowing out of their box,
In charge of the guard, that kindly man
Who, at the last moment, hauled into the van
That fortunate boy called Donald MacBrain
Who came to the station to catch the train
But saw the guard from Donibristle
Wave his flag and blow his whistle
To tell the driver,
Mr MacIver,
To start the train to Glasgow.

Now Donald was quick and Donald was neat
And Donald was nimble on his feet.
He caught the hens and he caught the cocks
And he put them back in their great big box.
The guard was pleased as pleased could be
And invited Donald to come to tea
On Saturday, at Donibristle
And let him blow his lovely whistle,
And said in all his life he'd never
Seen a boy so quick and clever,
And so did the driver,
Mr MacIver,
Who drove the train to Glasgow.

Wilma Horsburgh

The town and the countryside

The town
has streets and shoppers,
cars and vans and trucks.

    The countryside
    has fields and farmers,
    cows and pigs and ducks.

The town
has banks and bakeries
and markets stacked with goods.

    The countryside
    has sheep and shepherds,
    ponds and lanes and woods.

Wes Magee

Rush hour – London Underground

The train comes in like a dragon's tongue
And lots of strangers, old and young,
Tall and short and fat and thin,
Are rushing out and crushing in.

Cynthia Mitchell

CARtoon

Boot a-bulging, roof rack rocking,
Dad is driving, Katy's coughing,
Mum has migraine, Granny's grumpy,
Baby's bawling (Gran's lap's lumpy).
Sarah swears and sicks up sweeties, Dan the dog is wanting wee-wees.
All around are cars and cases, cones, congestion, furious faces
hauling homeward, slowly, slowly, from a fortnight's (hardly holy!)
"BUMPER Bargain Break-A-Way". *We never left the motorway!*

Gina Douthwaite

Traffic jam

Roar-roaring
Engines running
Horns hooting
Brakes grinding
Gears grating
Rev-revving
Creep, creeping
Overheating
Long waiting
Traffic jam.

Anne English

Stuck here forever

1st gear,
       2nd gear,
              3rd gear – NEVER,
Are we to be stuck in this traffic jam FOREVER!

With
Cars slowing and traffic growing,
Bumpers nudging, hardly budging.
Stop – start, stop – start, NO OVERTAKING!
Stop – start, stop – start, CONTINUAL BRAKING!

1st gear,
       2nd gear,
              3rd gear – NEVER,
Are we to be stuck in this traffic jam FOREVER!

With
Babies crying and others sighing,
Drivers glaring and horns blaring.
HONK! HONK! HONK! PEEP! PEEP! PEEP!
CARS, CARS, CARS like SHEEP, SHEEP, SHEEP!

1st gear,
       2nd gear,
              3rd gear – NEVER,
Are we to be stuck in this traffic jam FOREVER!

Engines turning and fumes burning,
Petrol oxidizing and pollution rising.
SMOKE! SMOKE! SMOKE! CHOKE! CHOKE! CHOKE!
A solution to pollution would be a masterstroke.

1st hour,
       2nd hour,
              3rd hour's gone.
I'LL BE ANOTHER YEAR OLDER BEFORE WE MOVE ON!

Ian Souter

Uncle Joe's jalopy

When you're riding in my Uncle Joe's jalopy,
Better hang on tight 'cos the roads are pretty choppy
When you're travelling in that car.

It's a dumpy little jumpy little bumpy little number
And it doesn't pay to sleep and it doesn't pay to slumber
And you'd best not go too far
When you're travelling in that car.

It's got holes in the roof the snow has snowed through,
Holes in the floor you can see the road through,
Holes in the dash the petrol's flowed through –
Pretty scary car!

It's got broken springs – brakes on the blink –
Wheels that wobble – fumes that stink –
And the windscreen's turned as black as ink
So you can't see where you are
When you're travelling in that car:
So you'd best not go too far!

But don't you *criticize* that jalopy
Or Uncle Joe will get mighty stroppy
'Cos he really likes that car!

When he's at the wheel of that old bone-shaker
He thinks he's a Grand Prix record-breaker –
He thinks he's a motor star!

When he bangs round corners on two square wheels,
Folks on the pavement take to their heels
'Cos they don't feel as safe as Uncle Joe feels
When he's travelling in that car:

And as for me, I can't wait for the day
When the wheels fall off and the roof blows away
And Uncle Joe will just have to say,
'Well, that's the end of that car:
It really can't go too far!'

Kit Wright

Cycling down the street to meet my friend John

On my bike and down our street,
Swinging round the bend,
Whizzing past the Library,
Going to meet my friend.

Silver flash of spinning spokes,
Whirr of oily chain,
Bump of tyre on railway line
Just before the train.

The road bends sharp at Pinfold Lane
Like a broken arm,
Brush the branches of the trees
Skirting Batty's Farm.

Tread and gasp and strain and bend
Climbing Gallows' Slope,
Flying down the other side
Like an antelope.

Swanking into Johnnie's street,
Cycling hands on hips,
Past O'Connors corner shop
That always smells of chips.

Bump the door of his backyard
Where we always play,
Lean my bike and knock the door,
'Can John come out to play?'

Gareth Owen

Do as you're told

I've a cold in the head
And mum says, 'Stay in bed.'
    Sniffles and sneezes
    Coughs and wheezes.
She brings drinks, hot and cold,
And says, 'Do as you're told.'
    Sniffles and sneezes
    Coughs and wheezes.
I keep warm with the covers
Right up to my chin
Then she opens the window
To let cold air in!
    Sniffles and sneezes
    Coughs and wheezes.
But you do as you're told
When you have a bad cold.

Anne English

Bones

Brains
spend   a   lifetime   in
prison, within the   thick walls
of your *skull*, safe from attack,
unless a bad crack should render
their   reasoning   dull.   To   visit, a
vertabrae ladder, leads through a cage made
of *ribs* - count as you climb   one pair   at a
time. We've all got the same - so no fibs!
Try clashing those *scapula* blades, that keep both
your shoulders in shape.   Would these be stronger
if arms were longer and man walked around like
an ape? Don't laugh at your *humerus* bone -
without it, from elbow, below, it's obvious *ulna*
and *radius*   would crash to   the concrete
(ho! ho!).   Twisted   wrists,
broken?   hang   limply,
dangling   down   *meta*-
carpals.   If   *phalanges*
flex then   the inde x   finger's
O.K. - but it startles! A *pelvis* is really quite
hip, when dancing   away to the beat.
It   swivels   and   pivots and quivers
and anchors   both   legs to your seat
by using a *socket-and-ball* to lock in the head
of the *femur*. Then there's a need, I'm sure
you're agreed,   for knee caps   - *patella*
would seem a suitable bone to connect
with the *tibia/fibula* pair, one thick
and one thin but both ending in
meta-   *tarsals*
and   toes
and   that's
where this stands as a *skeleton*
lesson - a framework in which
you might hang organs or
fix, in place, appendix.
Your scaffold - for
body   of
MAN.

Gina Douthwaite

Chicken spots

I've got these really itchy spots
they're climbing on my tummy
they're on my head
they're on my tail
and it isn't very funny.
They came to see me yesterday
– a few the day before
fifty on my bottom
and twenty on my jaw.

I've a prize one on my toe
a dozen on my knee
and now they're on my thingy
– I think there's thirty-three.

I count them every evening
I give them names like Fred
    Charlie Di and Daisy
    Chunky Tom and Ted.

They're really awful spotties
they drive me itchy mad
the sort of itchy scratchings
I wish I never had.
Nobby's worst at itching
Lizzie's awful too
and – if you come to see me
then I'll give a few to you...
    I'll give you Di and Daisy –
    I'll give you Jane and Ted
    a bucket full of itchers
    to take home to your bed...
        You can give them to your sister
        I don't care what you do
        Give them to a teacher
        or send them to the zoo.
        I don't care where you take 'em
        I don't care where they go...
            stick them up the chimney
            or in the baby's po.
            Take them to a farmyard.
            Find a chicken pen,
            say that they're a present
                with love
                    from me
                        ...to them.

Peter Dixon

Favouritism

When we caught measles
It wasn't fair –
My brother collected
Twice his share.

He counted my spots:
'One hundred and twenty!'
Which sounded to me
As if I had plenty.

Then I counted his –
And what do you think?
He'd two hundred and thirty-eight,
Small, round and pink!

I felt I'd been cheated
So, 'count mine again!'
I told him, and scowled
So he dared not complain.

'One hundred and twenty' –
The same as before...
In our house, he's youngest
And he *always* gets more.

Trevor Harvey

Sneezing

Sneeze on Monday,
        sneeze for danger.
Sneeze on Tuesday,
        meet a stranger.
Sneeze on Wednesday,
        sneeze for a letter.
Sneeze on Thursday,
        feeling better.
Sneeze on Friday,
        sneeze for sorrow.
Sneeze on Saturday,
        see your sweetheart tomorrow.

Anonymous

Bacteria

There are tens of thousands
on each one of us –
tinier than the tiniest fly,
so light we can't feel them.
Yet there they are –
like plump cows or sheep,
the colour of thin milk,
wandering across the broad fields of our skin
between the huge reeds of our hair,
nibbling.
    And I like to think of them there
so calmly browsing, cleaning me up.
It makes me feel like a farmer, a world,
to have so many creatures
keeping alive on me,
so many creatures
that think of me as home.

Dave Calder

Epitaph

Here lies John Smith, exactly eight,
Who was given a handsome chemistry set.
Here also lies his sister, Maria,
Or what was left of them after the fire.

Roy Fuller

Crystals

First, in saucers we spread salt.
Our imagination turns

its shimmer into spoil heaps
drawn from far-off diamond mines

beneath the tawny plain
of Africa. We hold this dream

until the drench of water
vanquishes their fire.

A string of disappearing pools,
we range them along windowsills

and the sun steals in on lion's paws
to lap away their drink.

Our teacher mixes 'poison'
in a glass apart for safety;

it attracts us like a blinding sky
of fierce, ice-shattering blue.

Our waterholes days later
have dried up to brittle crusts

of sharp-edged crystals
glittering like splintered glass.

Ice-wonder fills our eyes
almost to snow-blinding.

Our teacher's soft brown hand
shows diamonds of blue

deeper than sky or sea.
Her eyes sparkle ice and fire.

Barrie Wade

THROUGH THE YEAR

A child's calendar

No visitors in January.
A snowman smokes a cold pipe in the yard.

They stand about like ancient women,
The February hills.
They have seen many a coming and going, the hills.

In March Moorfea is littered
With knock-kneed lambs.

Daffodils at the door in April,
Three shawled Marys.
A lark splurges in galilees of sky.

And in May
A russet stallion shoulders the hill apart.
The mares tremble.

The June bee
Bumps in the pane with a heavy bag of plunder.

Strangers swarm in July
With cameras, binoculars, bird books.

He thumped the crag in August,
A blind blue whale.

September crofts get wrecked in blond surges.
They struggle, the harvesters.
They drag loaf and ale-kirn into winter.

In October the fishmonger
Argues, pleads, threatens at the shore.

Nothing in November
But tinkers at the door, keening, with cans.

Some December midnight
Christ, lord, lie warm in our byre.
Here are stars, an ox, poverty enough.

George Mackay Brown

The months of the year

January brings the snow;
Makes our feet and fingers glow.

February brings the rain,
Thaws the frozen ponds again.

March brings breezes, loud and shrill,
Stirs the dancing daffodil.

April brings the primrose sweet,
Scatters daisies at our feet.

May brings flocks of pretty lambs,
Skipping by their fleecy dams.

June brings tulips, lilies, roses;
Fills the children's hands with posies.

Hot July brings cooling showers,
Strawberries and gilly-flowers.

August brings the sheaves of corn,
Then the Harvest home is borne.

Warm September brings the fruit,
Sportsmen then begin to shoot.

Fresh October brings the pheasant;
Then to gather nuts is pleasant.

Dull November brings the blast,
Then the leaves are falling fast.

Chill December brings the sleet,
Blazing fire and Christmas treat.

Sara Coleridge

Twelve months in the year

Thirty days has September,
April, June and November.
All the rest have thirty-one,
Excepting February alone,
And that has twenty-eight days clear
And twenty-nine in each leap year.

Anonymous

Chinese New Year

Dragons, lions,
Red and gold.
In the New Year,
Out the Old.

Banners flying,
Street parades.
Good surviving,
Evil fades.

Fire crackers,
Lanterns swing.
Fifteen days
To dance and sing.

Dragons, lions,
Red and gold.
In the New Year
Out the Old.

Wendy Larmont

First sight

Lambs that learn to walk in snow
When their bleating clouds the air
Meet a vast unwelcome, know
Nothing but a sunless glare.
Newly stumbling to and fro
All they find, outside the fold,
Is a wretched width of cold.

As they wait beside the ewe,
Her fleeces wetly caked, there lies
Hidden round them, waiting too,
Earth's immeasurable surprise.
They could not grasp it if they knew,
What so soon will wake and grow
Utterly unlike the snow.

Philip Larkin

Coming out of hibernation

Black bats hang in barns,
their wings folded
like old umbrellas.

Snoring hedgehogs sleep
curled up,
like hairbrushes
beneath crisp leaves.

Grey squirrels dream
in dreys of scrambled twigs.

Toads squat,
their eyelids drawn down,
as still as stones
tucked beneath
damp earth.

Sly spring sunlight
creeps through clouds,
bulbs break the earth
and the world wears
a new coat.

Bats stretch their creased wings
and blink their way
from hollow tree stumps.

Hedgehogs uncurl
and sniff,
sipping the sunlight.

The blotched toad
gulps in warm air;
he puffs his wrinkled cheeks
like an old man.

The squirrel stretches
her arched back
and tests a branch.
Like a rat she runs
to find her acorn stash.

The world rolls on to its side
and stretches out its legs.
It reaches for its sunglasses
and rubs its earthy hands.

The spring sings out loud.

Pie Corbett

Pancake day

Mix a pancake,
Stir a pancake,
    Pop it in the pan.
Fry the pancake,
Toss the pancake,
    Catch it if you can.

Christina Rossetti

A change in the year

It is the first mild day in March:
    Each minute sweeter than before,
The redbreast sings from the tall larch
    That stands beside our door.

There is a blessing in the air,
    Which seems a sense of joy to yield
To the bare trees, and mountain bare,
    And grass in the green field.

William Wordsworth

Loveliest of trees

Loveliest of trees, the cherry now
Is hung with bloom along the bough,
And stands about the woodland ride
Wearing white for Eastertide.

Now, of my threescore years and ten,
Twenty will not come again,
And take from seventy springs a score,
It only leaves me fifty more.

And since to look at things in bloom
Fifty springs are little room,
About the woodlands I will go
To see the cherry hung with snow.

A.E. Housman

Easter

The year turns at Easter time.

Button buds collect on the branches
and like a sprinkling of young yellow suns,
bright daffodils colour
the hibernating fields and hedgerows.

The year turns, slowly and silently, into Spring
and everywhere the new born chicks, lambs and fledglings
struggle to be seen, heard or noticed.
Out of the grey, bare days of weak winter
the sacred strength of Spring emerges.

The year turns and Mother Earth lifts her ashen face
to the pale blue of a brightening sky.
In celebration she pushes up
the timeclocks of the ages –
a flourish of flowers, a blast of blossom.

John Rice

Menu....for 1st April

Solid soup
Coddled carrots
Roast cabbage
Molten beans
Poached potatoes
Fried gravy
Stewed bread
Baked butter
Barbecued ice-cream
Boiled biscuits
Curried cheese
Turtled tea

Eat the lot
That's the rule
Knock it back
APRIL FOOL

Wes Magee

from... Home thoughts, from abroad

Oh, to be in England
Now that April's there,
And whoever wakes in England
Sees, some morning, unaware,
That the lowest boughs and the brushwood sheaf
Round the elm-tree bole are in tiny leaf,
While the chaffinch sings on the orchard bough,
in England – now!

And after April, when May follows,
And the whitethroat builds, and all the swallows!
Hark, where my blossomed pear-tree in the hedge
Leans to the field and scatters on the clover
Blossoms and dewdrops – at the bent spray's edge –
That's the wise thrush; he sings each song twice over,
Lest you should think he never could recapture
The first fine careless rapture!
And though the fields look rough with hoary dew,
All will be gay when noontide wakes anew
The buttercups, the little children's dower
– Far brighter than this gaudy melon-flower!

Robert Browning

Laughing song

When the green woods laugh with the voice of joy,
And the dimpling stream runs laughing by;
When the air does laugh with our merry wit,
And the green hill laughs with the noise of it;

When the meadows laugh with lively green,
And the grasshopper laughs in the merry scene,
When Mary and Susan and Emily
With their sweet round mouths sing 'Ha, Ha, He!'

When the painted birds laugh in the shade,
When our table with cherries and nuts is spread,
Come live and be merry, and join with me,
To sing the sweet chorus of 'Ha, Ha, He!'

William Blake

The cuckoo

Cuckoo,
Cuckoo,
What do you do?

In April
I open my bill.

In May
I sing night and day.

In June
I change my tune.

In July
Away I fly.

In August
Go I must.

Anonymous

Holi

Under the full spring moon
Lord Krishna
watched young Rahda,
her downy beauty
delicate as pollen in the air,

a slim girl
in the slender light.

Krishna threw powder,
coloured powder
soft and mischievous as love
under the liquid moon;

through shadowed veils
her eyes danced.

New flowers bloomed
next day in Krishna's garden,
frail graceful girls
dancing their stories
to the powdered bees.

Irene Rawnsley

The caterpillar

Brown and furry
Caterpillar in a hurry,
Take your walk
To the shady leaf or stalk,
Or what not,
Which may be the chosen spot.
No toad to spy you,
Hovering bird of prey pass by you;
Spin and die,
To live again a butterfly.

Christina Rossetti

Early

In summer sometimes I'm up early:
Six o'clock my alarm's set to bleep
And I dress and go quietly downstairs
Leaving the family asleep.

And by the back door I put shoes on,
Turn the key – will it click today...? No.
Open the door – it creaks slightly –
And into the garden I go.

And I stand in a spell of stillness,
Into which a few birds calmly call,
In a misty, mysterious garden
That's not really our garden at all.

Now, everything in it is dreaming,
As I walk treading prints in the dew
Past the trees in their secret silence...
And I feel as if I'm dreaming too.

Back indoors they're all stirring – and grumpy –
And Dad says, 'Oh, you're here as well.
Why on earth did you get up so early?'
And I make some excuse. I don't tell.

Eric Finney

Adlestrop

Yes, I remember Adlestrop –
The name, because one afternoon
Of heat, the express-train drew up there
Unwontedly. It was late June.

The steam hissed. Someone cleared his throat.
No one left and no one came
On the bare platform. What I saw
Was Adlestrop – only the name

And willows, willow-herb, and grass,
And meadowsweet, and haycocks dry,
No whit less still and lonely fair
Than the high cloudlets in the sky.

And for that minute a blackbird sang
Close by, and round him, mistier,
Farther and farther, all the birds
Of Oxfordshire and Gloucestershire.

Edward Thomas

The tastes of summer

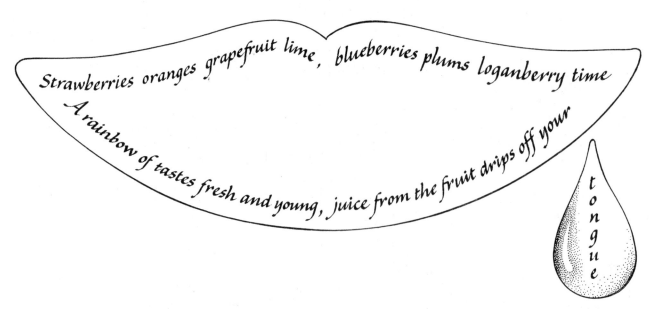

Strawberries oranges grapefruit lime, blueberries plums loganberry time
A rainbow of tastes fresh and young, juice from the fruit drips off your
tongue

Laurelle Rond

The Fourth of July

On the Fourth of July – yes,
　　the Fourth of July –
you may run up the flag
　　　till it's high

　　　　　　till it's high,
and throw all that you've got
　　　to the top

　　　　　　of the sky....

For it's freedom we wanted
　　　and freedom we sought,
and it's freedom we cherish
　　　and freedom we bought:
we'll share it

　　　　　and wear it
whoever runs by –
　　　till they know

　　　　　　as they go
it's the Fourth of July....
　　　INDEPENDENCE is surely
the core of our cry,
　　　and we'll sing it, and ring it,
the Fourth of July!

My mother saw a dancing bear

My mother saw a dancing bear
By the schoolyard, a day in June.
The keeper stood with chain and bar
And whistle-pipe, and played a tune.

And bruin lifted up its head
And lifted up its dusty feet,
And all the children laughed to see
It caper in the summer heat.

They watched as for the Queen it died.
They watched it march. They watched it halt.
They heard the keeper as he cried,
'Now, roly-poly!' 'Somersault!'

And then, my mother said, there came
The keeper with a begging-cup,
The bear with burning coat of fur,
Shaming the laughter to a stop.

They paid a penny for the dance.
But what they saw was not the show;
Only, in bruin's aching eyes,
Far-distant forests, and the snow.

Charles Causley

What happens to the sunsets?

What happens to the sunsets,
The shiny pink and gold bits,
The trimmings of the day?
They're swept into the duskpan
And tipped into the skybin.
Night carries them away.

Sue Cowling

from...Pied beauty

Glory be to God for dappled things –
For skies of couple-colour as a brinded cow;
For rose-moles all in stipple upon trout that swim;
Fresh-firecoal chestnut-falls; finches' wings;
Landscape plotted and pieced – fold, fallow, and plough;
And all trades, their gear and tackle and trim.

Gerard Manley Hopkins

Autumn fires

In the other gardens
        And all up the vale,
From the autumn bonfires
        See the smoke trail!

Pleasant summer over
        And all the summer
flowers,
The red fire blazes,
        The grey smoke towers.

Sing a song of seasons!
        Something bright in all!
Flowers in the summer,
        Fires in the fall!

Robert Louis Stevenson

Autumn

A touch of cold in the Autumn night –
I walked abroad,
And saw the ruddy moon lean over a hedge
Like a red-faced farmer.
I did not stop to speak, but nodded,
And round about were the wistful stars
With white faces like town children.

T.E. Hulme

The Harvest Queen

**(or Corn Mother, who controls
all the seasons)**

Since sown
in spring
she's grown.
Sun has warmed
and rains
have fed her.
Winds have blown.

Crows have flown
above the fields now shorn
of ripened corn.
Drowsy poppies shown
their dazzling red.

Blackberries glisten.
Swallows gather
from the eaves.
The sheaves
of wheat collected.
The first leaves fall.

The golden corn
is Queen of all
the Harvest. The store
is full. Winter is
provided for.

Ann Bonner

Divali

Ravana's gone,
the demon king has done!
Now once again
with feasting and with prayer
we light a thousand guiding lamps
to welcome Rama here
and bring good fortune
for the coming year.

Judith Nicholls

Something told the wild geese

Something told the wild geese
It was time to go.
Though the fields lay golden
Something whispered – 'Snow'.
Leaves were green and stirring,
Berries, lustre-glossed,
But beneath warm feathers
Something cautioned – 'Frost'.

All the sagging orchards
Steamed with amber spice,
But each wild breast stiffened
At remembered ice.
Something told the wild geese
It was time to fly –
Summer sun was on their wings,
Winter in their cry.

Rachel Field

The man outside

There's a man in the street
And I don't like his stare
And I don't like the look
Of his prickly hair
And I don't like the size
Or his shape, he's too thin,
And I don't like his slouch
Or his lopsided grin,
But I'm not at all scared –
Do you want to know why?
It's November the Fifth
And his name is Guy.

Richard Edwards

A Hallowe'en pumpkin

They chose me from my brother: 'That's the
Nicest one,' they said,
And they carved me out a face and put a
Candle in my head.

And they set me on the doorstep. Oh, the
Night was dark and wild;
But when they lit the candle, then I
Smiled!

Dorothy Aldis

The 5th of November

Please to remember
The 5th of November,
Gunpowder, treason, and plot.
I see no reason
Why gunpowder treason
Should ever be forgot.

Anonymous

Jack Frost

He creeps through the grasses,
He'll catch as catch can,
Cold in his bones, he's a
Slippery man.

Fingering patterns
Of spidery lace,
He steals away warmth
And leaves ice in its place.

Theresa Heine

Snowfall

Ice-jewelled fir trees in a lonely coppice stand
Frosty heads silhouetted against a whitewashed land.
Branches, bowed by winter's weight, strive to touch the ground.
Across the starlit countryside only silence can be found.

Janis Priestley

Sheep in winter

The sheep get up and make their many tracks
And bear a load of snow upon their backs,
And gnaw the frozen turnip to the ground
With sharp quick bite, and then go noising round
The boy that pecks the turnips all the day
And knocks his hands to keep the cold away
And laps his legs in straw to keep them warm
And hides behind the hedges from the storm.
The sheep, as tame as dogs, go where he goes
And try to shake their fleeces from the snows,
Then leave their frozen meal and wander round
The stubble stack that stands beside the ground,
And lie all night and face the drizzling storm
And shun the hovel where they might be warm.

John Clare

I glide over the snow

I glide over the snow
on my toboggan
like a drop of water
slipping off a wing

the white wing
of a huge sea-bird
or a gathering cloud

a cloud that darkens
then huffs and puffs
itself into a temper

letting itself go
in a fall of snow
to land on places
my toboggan goes

Sue Stewart

In winter I like...

Soup in a cup and hot buttered toast,
All the surprises of the Christmas post,
Soft woolly jumper up to my chin,
A light at the window when I'm coming in.

Anne English

Snowed in

The house wears a muffler.
The road outside is still.
The postman hasn't called.
His van can't climb the hill.

The puddles are polished
and powdered with snow.
The trees dressed in white
for the Christmas Card Show.

Pie Corbett

A thinking Christmas

A turkey dinner
at Christmas
is great!

THINK

Somewhere...a boy
with an empty plate.

The Christmas tree lights
shine red, green
and gold.

THINK

Somewhere...a girl
shivering and cold.

Presents, and parties!
Yes, *that's*
Christmas Day!

THINK

Somewhere...a babe
asleep in the hay.

Wes Magee

New Year

This night
of all the nights
is the year's last.
All, all
the other nights
are gone, are past...

After
the evening, with
its fading light,
put the lid
on the hour
and close it tight.

Close up
your tired eye;
close up the day.
Bid the old year
Goodbye,
and come away.

Jean Kenward

SCHOOL DAYS

I've got an apple ready

My hair's tightly plaited;
I've a bright blue bow;
I don't want my breakfast,
And now I must go.

My satchel's on my shoulder;
Nothing's out of place;
And I've got an apple ready,
Just in case.

So it's, 'Goodbye, Mother!'
And off down the street;
Briskly at first
On pit-a-pat feet,

But slow and more slow
As I reach the tarred
Trackway that runs
By Hodson's Yard;

For it's there sometimes
Bill Craddock waits for me
To snatch off my beret
And throw it in a tree.

Bill Craddock leaning
On Hodson's rails;
Bill with thin hands
And dirty nails;

Bill with a front tooth
Broken and bad;
His dark eyes cruel,
And somehow sad.

Often there are workmen,
And then he doesn't dare;
But this morning I feel
He'll be there.

At the corner he will pounce...
But quickly I'll say,
'Hallo, Bill; have an apple!' –
In an ordinary way.

I'll push it in his hand
And walk right on;
And when I'm round the corner
I'll run!

John Walsh

It's school today

I wake up early, it's school today,
I'll get up early and be on my way.
I wash my face,
I brush my hair,
I hang my nightdress on the chair.

The breakfast table is all set,
I'll eat it quickly and feed my pet,
I wave to mum
and shut the gate:
I'll have to hurry, it's half past eight.
The bus has gone,
I'll run to school.
I pass the shops
and the swimming pool.
I reach the gate: it's five past nine.
Goodness me!
I'm just in time.

Anonymous

Who?

Who's always there come rain or shine,
From eight o'clock till ten past nine?
Who's back again at half past three
As we are going home for tea?
Who wears a coat that's long and white,
And cap with badge that's big and bright?
Who's always cheerful, always nice?
Whose banner bears a strange device?
Who teaches us the Highway Code,
And sees us safely 'cross the road?
Who is it makes the traffic stop?
O Lady of the Lollipop!

Colin West

School daze

Our	School days start with playground noise,
with	Children racing, shouting boys.
Now	Here's the teacher bang on time;
he	Opens jaws, 'Get into line!'
But	Outside the gate a last girl crawls.
'Ann!	Late again!' the teacher bawls.
Then	Doors slam shut, and classrooms shake.
Our	All-action school is wide awake.
Some	Zoos, I think, have calmer ways
but we	Effect a real school daze.

Wes Magee

Conversation piece

Late again Blenkinsop?
What's the excuse this time?
Not my fault sir.
Who's fault is it then?
Grandma's sir.
Grandma's. What did she do?
She died sir.
Died?
She's seriously dead all right sir.
That makes four grandmothers this term.
And all on P.E. days Blenkinsop.
I know. It's very upsetting sir.
How many grandmothers have you got Blenkinsop?
Grandmothers sir? None sir.
None?
All dead sir.
And what about yesterday Blenkinsop?
What about yesterday sir?
You missed maths.
That was the dentist sir.
The dentist died?
No sir. My teeth sir.
You missed the test Blenkinsop.
I'd been looking forward to it too sir.
Right, line up for P.E.
Can't sir.
No such word as can't. Why can't you?
No kit sir.
Where is it?
Home sir.
What's it doing at home?
Not ironed sir.
Couldn't you iron it?
Can't do it sir.
Why not?
My hand sir.
Who usually does it?
Grandma sir.
Why couldn't she do it?
Dead sir.

Gareth Owen

What is it?

I have twenty-eight faces,
    fifty-six ears.
Some parts of me are happy
    and some are close to tears.

Parts of me are topped with gold,
    parts with brown
and I am a strange many headed-creature
    in a strange town.

(answer: a new class of children)

Fred Sedgwick

Mr Whackem

Mr Whackem's a very good man,
    He goes to church on Sunday.
He prays that God will give him strength
    To whack the kids on Monday.

Anonymous

Miss Buss and Miss Beale

Miss Buss and Miss Beale
Cupid's darts do not feel.
Oh, how different from us
Are Miss Beale and Miss Buss.

Anonymous

In love?

Our Miss Gill
and Mr Scott
seem to like each other
rather a lot.
His class
and our class
are always going
on trips together.
Today we climbed
Tucker's Hill
in *dreadful* weather.
      'He held her hand.'
         'Never!'
      'He did. And they kissed.'
         'No!'
It turned terribly cold.
'I'm freezing,' said Jill.
It started to rain,
then there was sleet,
and then there was snow.

At least it was warm
on the coach
and we all sang.
Arrived at the school gate
just as the bell rang.
Off we trooped home.
At the street corner
I turned
and looked back.
So did Jill.
We watched
as our Miss Gill
crossed the car park
hand in glove
with Mr Scott.
      'They *are* in love,'
said Jill.
Yes, they do seem
to like each other
rather a lot.

Wes Magee

A Teacher from Leeds

There once was a teacher from Leeds
Who swallowed a packet of seeds
    In less than an hour
    Her nose was a flower
And her hair was a posy of weeds.

Anonymous

Teacher, teacher...

Teacher, teacher, don't be dumb,
Give me back my bubblegum.

    teacher, teacher
    you're the best
    when you wear
    that old string vest

Teacher, teacher, I declare
Tarzan's lost his underwear.

    teacher, teacher
    come here quick
    Stella Brown's
    been awful sick

Teacher, teacher, don't be mean,
Give me a dime for the coke machine.

    teacher, teacher
    no more school
    let's go down
    the swimming pool.

Anonymous

Mouse at assembly

A mouse came to assembly today –
Just as we'd got to
'All creatures great and small',
It came scuttling neatly along the wall.
As news of its arrival spread
It stopped dead;
Was struck by the strangeness of what it saw,
Turned,
And clockworked back to the Music Store.

Hands together for a prayer –
In the hush again he's there;
In the same well-oiled and legless manner
Travels a dozen feet
And dives under the piano.

No going on with assembly:
Buzz, excitement, standing on chairs –
Better this than hymns and prayers!

The Head,
Recovering from stupefaction,
Proves himself a man of action:
'Caretaker...two dustpans quick!
That, I think, should do the trick.'

And soon at each side of the piano
Is posted an alert dustpanner
Poised to scoop the nimble beast;
Suspense...not the least
Noise from the school...
'A few crashing chords to scare him out, please.
Preferable this to traps and cheese.'

But this mouse is no fool –
Emerges by the piano stool,
Avoiding the dustpans by a street,
Narrowly missing the pianist's feet;
Vanishes rapidly into the gloom
Of the caretaker's room.

Headmaster's jaw
Hits floor;
Smile disappears;
School cheers –
Hooray! Hooray!
Mouse lives to creep another day.

Eric Finney

The pocket calculator

Ready to go to work
The moment it sees the light,
The pocket calculator
Clears its memory
At a touch
And in the panel a nought
Comes out as a flower
Opens to the sun.

Of course, it's always right,
Whether it adds,
subtracts
or multiplies,
Or copies the mistakes I make.
But somehow it seems strange
That whether you lose or gain
Ninety-nine million,
Nine hundred and ninety-nine thousand,
Nine hundred and ninety-nine
Of pounds
Or anything
Its straightfaced look
Will never change.

Stanley Cook

The hard book

This is a hard book
in small print
with no pictures
and four columns on each page.

Every four lines or so
there is a number by the side
and for some reason some
words are in *italics*.

At the beginning of the book
there is a letter from
King James the First
especially to me, but

I must apologise
I have never read it.
It is too long, and, well,
doesn't look interesting.

It is the oldest book
I've ever touched,
and for some reason
I keep going back to it;

not to read you understand
just to turn the pages
catching the odd word
that's been dead for ages:

Melchizedek,
Og, Habbakuk, Nebuchadnezzar,
forever and ever amen.

David Scott

New notebook

Lines
in a new notebook
run, even and fine,
like telephone wires
across a snowy landscape.

With wet, black strokes
the alphabet settles between them,
comfortable as a flock of crows.

Judith Thurman

Two times table

Twice one are two,
Violets white and blue.

Twice two are four,
Sunflowers at the door.

Twice three are six,
Sweet peas on their sticks.

Twice four are eight,
Poppies at the gate.

Twice five are ten,
Pansies bloom again.

Twice six are twelve,
Pinks for those who delve.

Twice seven are fourteen,
Flowers of the runner bean.

Twice eight are sixteen,
Clinging ivy ever green.

Twice nine are eighteen,
Purple thistles to be seen.

Twice ten are twenty,
Hollyhocks in plenty.

Twice eleven are twenty-two,
Daisies wet with morning dew.

Twice twelve are twenty-four,
Roses...who could ask for more.

Anonymous

I am a full stop

I am a full stop.
At my command,
sentences halt.
At its peril,
a letter which follows me
forgets it should be a capital.
I place myself between words.
I create meaning.
When children ignore me,
I cause confusion.
I am a full stop.
Learn to control *me*
and the whole written world
is yours.

John Foster

Skipping song

The high skip,
The sly skip,
The skip like a feather,
The long skip,
The strong skip,
And the skip all together.

The slow skip,
The toe skip,
The skip double-double,
The fast skip,
The last skip,
And the skip against trouble.

Anonymous

The race

The race is just about to start...
Toeing the line with all the others
  heart pounding
  hands sweating
Waiting, waiting for the whistle....

The whistle blows, shrill!
You start to run
  feet pounding the lush, green grass
  fists clenched
Hot summer air rushes past your face
Making your chest burn.

Head held high, eyes front,
You run as if your life depended on it...
  glimpsing the winner's tape moving in the breeze
  you chase it – closer, closer still,
The others closer on your heels.

But as you feel the winner's tape
Dragging at your chest
  you hear the cheers!
  All fears now gone,
Lost in victory!

Jo Vernillo

Friends

As friends we
whisper,
discuss,
argue,
then float messages across crowded playgrounds
that only we know and understand.

As friends we
walk,
stumble,
run,
then sprint after each other,
so close we exchange shadows as we go.

As friends we
laugh,
cry,
care,
taste each other's thoughts
and share each other's moods.

One girl, one boy,
one friendship to enjoy.
One lock, one key,
that's you and me!

Ian Souter

Counting out

Icker-backer
Soda-cracker
Icker-backer-boo
Un-lucky
Number nine
And
Out go you.

Anonymous

The fight

There's a fight on the playground today –
    Two big boys from Mr Magee's
Are knocking the daylights out of each other
    Under the trees.

The girls are silent and staring
    And Clare whispers, 'Stop it, Paul,'
As the fighting gets wilder, and feet jab out
    And fingers maul.

I watch, and I'm glad it's not Joe
    And me in that horrible space –
Not my stomach winded, not my nose bleeding,
    Not my burning face.

The sky is bright. Two planes fly
    Out from the base, while one
Boy holds the other down with his knee
    And breathes, 'You done?'

There's a fight on the playground today –
    Paul Topple from Mr Magee's
Is crushing the daylights out of John Randall
    Under the trees.

Fred Sedgwick

School dinners

If you stay to school
dinners
Better throw them aside;
A lot of kids didn't,
A lot of kids died.

The meat is made of iron,
The spuds are made of steel;
And if they don't get you,
The afters will.

Anonymous

James Bond comes to lunch

The day James Bond
came to lunch at our school
He
Dive bomb'd a sausage
Kung Fu'd a carrot
Machine gunn'd a fish-cake
Swam through the custard
And
Kissed Agnes the dinner lady.

Tom Edwards

From the classroom window

Sometimes, when heads are deep in books,
And nothing stirs,
The sunlight touches that far hill,
And its three dark firs;
Then on those trees I fix my eyes –
And teacher hers.

Together awhile we contemplate
The air-blue sky
And those dark tree-tops; till, with a tiny
Start and sigh,
She turns again to the printed page –
And so do I.

But our two thoughts have met out there
Where no school is –
Where, among call of birds and faint
Shimmer of bees,
They rise in sunlight, resinous, warm –
Those dark fir-trees!

John Walsh

I hear...

When I think of school
I hear
High shouts tossed
Like juggled balls in windy yards, and lost
In gutters, treetops, air.
And always, somewhere,
Piano-notes water-fall
And small sharp voices wail.
A monster-roar surges – 'Goal!'
The bell.
Then doors slam. There's the kick, scruff, stamp of shoes
Down corridors that trap and trail echoes.
Desk-tops thud with books, kit-bags,
A child's ghost screams as her chair's pushed back.
Laughter bubbles up and bursts.
Screech-owl whistles. Quick-fox quarrel-flares.
The voice barks 'QUIET!'
All sit. All wait.
Till scraped chalk shrieks
And whispers creep.
Cough. Ruler crack. Desk creak.
And furtive into the silence comes
A tiny mouse-scrabbling of pens.
Scamper. Stop. Scamper. Stop. Tiptoe.
And there, just outside the top window
As it if had never ceased to be
But only needed listening to
A scatter of birdsong, floating free.

Berlie Doherty

Poemspeak

When teacher reads a poem out loud
She has a special tone.
Like toffee cheese or plums-in-jam,
Or a wind-up gramophone.

I don't like poshed-up, snotty poems,
They get right up my nose.
Our teacher reads 'MacDonald's Farm'
Like 'Love's a red, red rose'.

Poems are for everyday,
Not made all la-di-dah.
They're fish and chips, or egg on toast,
Not quails and caviar.

They're happy, angry, sad, or fun,
In English, Thai or Russian.
But when *our* teacher reads poems wrong
They're boring as concussion.

Lucy Coats

Unfair

When we went over the park
Sunday mornings
to play football
we picked up sides.

Lizzie was our striker
because she had the best shot.

When the teachers
chose the school team
Marshy was our striker.

Lizzie wasn't allowed to play,
they said.

So she watched us lose, instead...

Michael Rosen

Our side of the playground

'This is our side of the playground,
What are you doing here?
You want to play football?
That's a laugh!
It's a boy's game. Got it clear?'

'Actually, Kev, she's pretty good.
Especially in goal.
I saw her down the rec. last night;
She was really in control.
Saved a penalty early on,
And from corners...can't she catch!
Dived several times
At their striker's feet –
Really kept us in the match.'

'Well, in that case...
Of course, it's actually
In goal where we're really weak.
I mean, anyone's got to be better
Than Baggs –
He couldn't play hide and seek.
Even a girl would be better than him...
Look, we've got to decide.
Let's take her on.
Hey, where's she gone?
Oh, she's gone back to *their* side.'

Eric Finney

from... The new boy's view of rugby

When first I played I nearly died.
　　The bitter memory still rankles –
They formed a scrum with *me* inside!
　　Some kicked the ball and some my ankles.
I did not like the game at all,
　　Yet, after all the harm they'd done me,
Whenever I came near the ball
　　They knocked me down and stood upon me.

Rupert Brooke

from...School's out

Girls scream,
Boys shout;
Dogs bark,
School's out.

W.H. Davies

Friday

Friday; the clock ticks on to four;
A week of school survived once more;
Teachers smiling, acting friendly,
Feeling, like the kids, weekendly.
Ahead, two days, and all that fun –
Untouched, intact, not yet begun;
Monday's a million miles away,
There's time to please yourself and play.
Nice-as-pie day, clear-blue-sky day:
Why can't all days feel like Friday?

Eric Finney

Homework

I love to do my homework,
It makes me feel so good.
I love to do exactly
As my teacher says I should.

I love to do my homework,
I never miss a day,
I even love the men in white
Who are taking me away.

Anonymous

A bonfire

Build a bonfire,
Build a bonfire,
Put the Head on the top.
Put the teachers in the middle
And let's burn
The lot.

Anonymous

Epitaph

A schoolmistress called Binks lies here.
She held her own for twenty year.
She pleaded, biffed, said: 'I'm your friend.'
But children got her in the end.

Roy Fuller

Index of Poets

Index of First Lines

Index of Themes

Acknowledgements

The publishers gratefully acknowledge permission to reproduce the following copyright material:

© Moira Andrew for 'Sea seasons' first published in *Language in Colour* by Moira Andrew (Belair Publications Ltd.), 'Balloon Fiesta' and 'Sleeping cats'; Bantum Doubleday Dell Publishing Group Inc. for 'Dancing teepees' By Calvin O'John from *The Whispering Wind* © 1972 The Institute of American Indian Arts; Blackie Children's Books for 'After a bath' © Aileen Fisher from *Up the Windy Hill* (Aberlard-Schumann) and 'The hard book' © 1989 David Scott from *How does it Feel?*; © Ann Bonner for 'The harvest queen' from *Let's Celebrate* (Oxford University Press); © Dave Calder for 'Bacteria'; © Lucy Coats for 'Poemspeak'; © Carol Coiffait for 'Homes fires', 'Reflections in a pond' and 'Who is he?'; © Stanley Cook for 'Clouds' and 'The pocket calculator'; © Pie Corbett for 'Coming out of hibernation' and 'Snowed in'; © Kay Cornish for '80';

© John Cotton for 'Dragonfly', 'Exploring the rock pool', 'Insect noises', 'In the kitchen' and 'The world with its countries'; © Sue Cowling for 'Bubblebath', 'Today in strong colours' and 'What happens to the sunsets?'; © Graeme Curry for 'James Bond comes to lunch' by Tom Edwards; Curtis Brown Ltd. for 'Sea timeless song' by Grace Nichols; André Deutsch Children's Books for 'The longest journey in the world' by Michael Rosen from *A Second Poetry Book*, 'From the winter wind' by Michael Rosen from *Mind your own Business*, 'I know someone who can' and 'Unfair' by Michael Rosen from *Quick Let's Get Out of Here*; © Peter Dixon for 'Chicken Spots' from *I Heard a Spider Sobbing*; © Berlie Doherty for 'I hear...' from *School's Out!* (Oxford University Press); © Gina Douthwaite for 'Bones', 'CARtoon', 'Fruit salad', 'Knickers', 'The road sweeper machine' and